(continued from front flap)

The plant pathologist is often a detective; through careful research and deduction he seeks to unravel the mysteries of plant disease. Using many fascinating examples Dr. Wellman introduces the reader to the vital and exciting field of plant pathology—a subject which will be important to man for as long as he enjoys the beauty of plants and the many benefits which they provide.

JACKET DESIGN BY GEO

Printed in the U.S.A.

PLANT DISEASES

The Natural History Press, publisher for The American Museum of Natural History, is a division of Doubleday & Company, Inc. Directed by a joint editorial board made up of members of the staff of both the Museum and Doubleday, the Natural History Press publishes books in all branches of the life and earth sciences, including anthropology and astronomy. The Natural History Press has its editorial offices at Doubleday & Company, Inc., 277 Park Avenue, New York, New York 10017, and its business offices at 501 Franklin Avenue, Garden City, New York 11530.

FREDERICK WELLMAN, the author of *Plant Diseases,* is a well-known plant pathologist who has traveled throughout the world searching for solutions to the problems of disease in growing plants. Since receiving his Ph.D. degree from the University of Wisconsin in 1928 Dr. Wellman has held many important posts, serving as plant pathologist for food industries in Central America and as Research Consultant for the U. S. Department of Agriculture in the Middle East and throughout Central and South America.

As a specialist in tropical plant pathology he has lectured at several universities and written many articles for scientific journals. Dr. Wellman is presently serving as Visiting Professor of Plant Pathology at North Carolina State University. He is also currently an adviser in the development of a broad international program of research and action to combat the recent appearance of coffee rust in Brazil. This is the first time that this dreaded plant disease has struck in South America, and its appearance could prove disastrous to the coffee-based economies.

Dr. Wellman's book *Plant Diseases* describes the fascinating work of the plant pathologist and traces the many factors that affect the health of growing plants—and the welfare of all of us who depend on them.

PLANT DISEASES

AN INTRODUCTION FOR THE LAYMAN

FREDERICK L. WELLMAN

PUBLISHED FOR THE AMERICAN MUSEUM OF NATURAL HISTORY

THE NATURAL HISTORY PRESS, GARDEN CITY, NEW YORK **NP**

CONSULTANT FOR THE PREPARATION OF THIS VOLUME:
DR. RICHARD M. KLEIN
LINE DRAWINGS BY THE AUTHOR

THIS BOOK

IS DEDICATED

TO

ANYONE

INTERESTED

IN IT

CONTENTS

FOREWORD

Everybody knows of the importance of microorganisms as causes of human and animal disease—yet the general public is almost totally unaware that plants are also subject to infection by microorganisms. The impact of plant diseases on the course of human history and their importance to the economy of nations today is even less well understood. This is true, notwithstanding the fact that a great mass of technical and scientific knowledge about the nature and control of plant diseases has accumulated during the past seventy-five to a hundred years since the concept of the germ theory of disease became firmly established.

Professor Wellman presents here, in one short volume, an interesting and informative account about crop plant diseases. It is written in a lucid, informal style which will appeal to the general reader and especially to all those who love plants. Many high school and even college biology teachers have small acquaintance with plant pathology and consequently many students graduate from college with little or no knowledge of the subject and no real idea of what a plant disease is or of its importance. Students who are trying to decide on some phase of biology in which to specialize often do not realize that plant pathology is a vital and fascinating pursuit which offers an opportunity for a career of service to all mankind. It will be no less appreciated, however, by those who have a professional or scientific interest in the subject. Professor Wellman's writing is based on wide experience gained over the past thirty-seven years as a research and practicing plant pathologist, including more than twenty years in many tropical and subtropical areas around the world.

He is motivated by a deep concern for underprivileged people everywhere, especially for those who have known the misery of hunger. His moving account of some of the great famines of the past calls attention anew to one of the greatest problems of our time. When one considers that the world population is expected to increase from about 3¼ billion at present to more than 6½ billion by the year 2000 and that two thirds of the people are currently underfed and underclothed, problems associated with agricultural production appear serious indeed. A basic understanding of plant diseases as they affect the mounting demands for food and fiber in an exploding population thus becomes the responsibility of every interested and concerned individual.

In this volume Professor Wellman provides a basis for this understanding and a much-needed enlightenment and clarification of an important phase of biology. He has rendered a great service to society and to his profession in bringing this information in such an enlightening manner.

D. E. Ellis
Professor and Head of Department
Department of Plant Pathology
North Carolina State University at Raleigh

PLANT DISEASES

PLANT DISEASES

PREFACE

A truck gardener climbs out of an old truck carrying bundles of wilted cabbage plants and a case of blotched tomatoes. A housewife angrily holds cellophane-wrapped packages of rotted potatoes, browned lettuce leaves, and rough and pitted carrot roots. A grain farmer drives in with weakened cornstalks, a sheaf of black marked straw, and a bag of musty grain. A wealthy orchardist takes you to examine trees weakened with leaf shot-hole, to see fruits that rot, branches that leak nauseous juices, or limbs that have cancerous swellings.

To a plant disease specialist, or plant pathologist, these are examples of dramatic human experiences. He has to know what causes each of these and other diseases and how they can be avoided or controlled. The greatest natural enemies of mankind are not fire, flood, earthquake, or storm, but diseases. Although there are already a large number of human diseases, now and then a new one appears.

Plants have diseases, too. One of the most common diseases known to attack man is the sniffles, or "a cold." It is due to infection by bacteria or viruses or from combinations of these. In plant pathology you learn that the same holds true—some of the most common plant diseases are also bacterial or viral or combinations of these. In human disease, the junction of one virus infection with another may greatly increase the infection's severity; in plants an attack by a combination of two or more viruses often causes death. Some bacteria or fungi cause sores and scabs on man's skin; there are bacteria and fungi, different ones, of course, that cause sores and scabs on plants. Some fungi, bacteria, and viruses gain entrance to the blood and have serious or fatal consequences in man; in plants, sap may be infected by blighting fungi, bacteria, and viruses. Man is affected by carcinoma or cancer; in plants attacked by certain bacteria and viruses, cells may run wild in uncontrolled growth that produces plant tumors. Man, however, is rarely infected by plant disease organisms.

In *The Origin of Species,* Charles Darwin commented eloquently about our survival. With infinite objectivity, he stood apart and regarded man as a part of the life that stirs, populates, and struggles on the earth. Of this struggle he said, "Nothing is easier to admit in words than the truth of the universal struggle for life, or more difficult—at least I have found it so—than constantly to bear this conclusion in mind." Man has advanced a great deal since Darwin's day, and part of our biological success has resulted from the development of the modern science of plant pathology expressly for protecting crops required by humanity. Even when experiments by plant disease specialists appear to onlookers most mystifying, they are useful and needed in gaining the knowledge we should have for plant pathology—all for the great purpose of insuring human survival.

The study of plant diseases (plant pathology) is a stimulating and important pursuit. The profession has proved itself in the past and present, and so it will in the future. The plant pathologist's work has progressed from ancient guess and stumbling to a logical science, based on experimental findings resulting in knowledge of what has to be done to control plant disease. It is to plant pathology that modern man looks to insure himself freedom from periodic famine.

This is not a doctor's medical book for plants, nor is it a cookbook full of recipes for sprays and chemical mixtures to treat sick roses, geraniums, tomatoes, or anything else. What I have presented here is a modest survey of the plant diseases that destroy plant production. I am especially grateful for the encouragement of Don E. Ellis. Any mistakes are of course the author's, but Professor Ellis, Robert Aycock, J. C. Walker, and Nash N. Winstead read portions of the manuscript while in progress and made valuable suggestions. David J. Rogers and Richard M. Klein aided as editors. At all times the careful attention as reader and critic by Dora Wellman was invaluable. She and Geraldine Winstead reviewed it from the standpoint of nontechnical readers. Finally, Joyce Johnson has been patient and considerate in helping on the book's preparation.

Frederick L. Wellman
Department of Plant Pathology
North Carolina State University at Raleigh

1

FAMINE

There are many plant diseases that have destroyed important food crops causing poverty, misery, hunger, and, finally, the ugliest thing in all human experience, famine. To some it may seem that famine is a matter of ancient history, but, because plant diseases still exist, hunger and famine are always present somewhere on this earth. It has been so since the beginning of humanity, and the end is not yet in sight. Even a prepared observer is overwhelmed and oppressed when he encounters famine. It is so horrible that it is easy to sympathize with the belief of ancient man that it was the worst curse of the gods.

I have seen and smelled villages in the last stages of famine. Human bodies, reduced to one third their normal weight, were horribly emaciated. The stark skin and bones of the chest and stomach sometimes were in terrible contrast to painfully swollen, grotesque, and roughened legs. The rags worn by the people were filthy beyond description because the wearers lacked the energy required for the elementary matters of cleanliness. To me, privileged, fed, and protected, the sight seemed an impossibility.

Famines erase all family ties. At first, effects may be slow; as a Psalm says, "They that die by famine die by inches." The old men and women waste away first, then youngsters and infants;

those in middle life struggle on longest. Famine-stricken persons apparently lose any feeling of affection, as parents fight away their own dying children for a sorry morsel of rotten food. There have been millions upon millions that have died in famines, and, it should be repeated, this situation can be found to this day. All will agree that, as Sir William Osler so well put it, "Humanity has but three great enemies: fever, famine, and war."

Famine in a far corner of the earth rarely makes the front-page headlines; it may be in a country where there is no news medium. It can begin when, one year, villagers who have been growing a successful, staple food crop for generations suddenly find a diseased place in a field. In two years it spreads throughout the land. Stern measures must be taken, and seed must be reserved for planting, with what is left divided for food among everyone sharing alike. When the disease hits a third time, the hungered and weakened know the end is near. Only help from the outside can save them. In modernized parts of the world, famine has not been widespread for some time, because transportation and communication with more fortunate people is so much improved. But we will never be absolutely immune from the threat of famine, for there is an ever-present danger of crop-plant diseases.

Millennia before we had any records, bacterial and fungal diseases developed on the earth. Archaeologists have found imprints, remains, and fossils of plants which were infected with parasitic fungi that flourished more than eighty million years ago. Parasites had already become well established when man appeared on earth millions of years later.

Properly interpreted, we can surmise from folk tales passed down from father to son and from tribe to tribe that plant diseases were causing serious crop failures in civilizations whose very names are now unknown. With the development of written records, the picture becomes quite clear: Man has been troubled with diseases of his crops since he left the nomadic existence of the hunter and began to develop agriculture as a way of life. Ancient scribes of the Sumerians, Hittites, pre-Mosaic Hebrews, the Sons of Elam, and Chinese of the Han dynasty feared famine more than they did war. Some of the more devastating plant diseases were mentioned by name in ancient Hebrew writings and, later, in the Old Testament. One of the worst recorded famines centered about Rome in 436 B.C. Even earlier, according to the Old Testament, one of the plagues visited upon Egypt was crop failure and famine. At about the time of Christ, crops again rotted in the Nile Valley, and large numbers of Egyptians died. It is likely that the prayer containing the phrase, "Give us this day our daily bread" comes down to us from the experience of our forefathers with famine.

A Greek of the Golden Age, Theophrastus, wrote accounts of diseases we know as olive knot, fig scab, fruit and root rot of figs, cereal rusts, rot of chick pea, grain moldiness, bean seed decay, canker and mildew of cumin, the strangling activity of the dodder, and parasitism of trees by the mistletoe. A few centuries later, the Roman savant, Pliny, attempted to catalogue and to explain the causes and dangers of plant diseases. The high priests and priestesses of the Roman gods prayed that Apollo, god of the sun, would shield the fields from the dread rusts, mildews, and rots. Each spring, a series of propitiatory ceremonies was held to ward off the blight-controlling twins, Rubigus and Rubigo. Astrologists attempted to foretell the coming of floods, hot winds, and, especially, the plague of the Great-Crop-Disease.

THE GREAT-CROP-DISEASE

The terrible Great-Crop-Disease was known by a number of names, some loathsome and of obscene connotation. One name is translated as "mildew" and "rust." How often grain crops were destroyed by the Great-Crop-Disease during prehistoric times no one will ever know. It was probably a factor in the slow development of early civilization. It is impossible to be absolutely sure what the Great-Crop-Disease was. It was probably a combination of root rots and leaf infections (FIGS. 1 AND 2). Wheat rust alone will completely destroy a crop unless intelligent control measures are applied. Add, then, a root rot along with other leaf and grain diseases and the results are catastrophic.

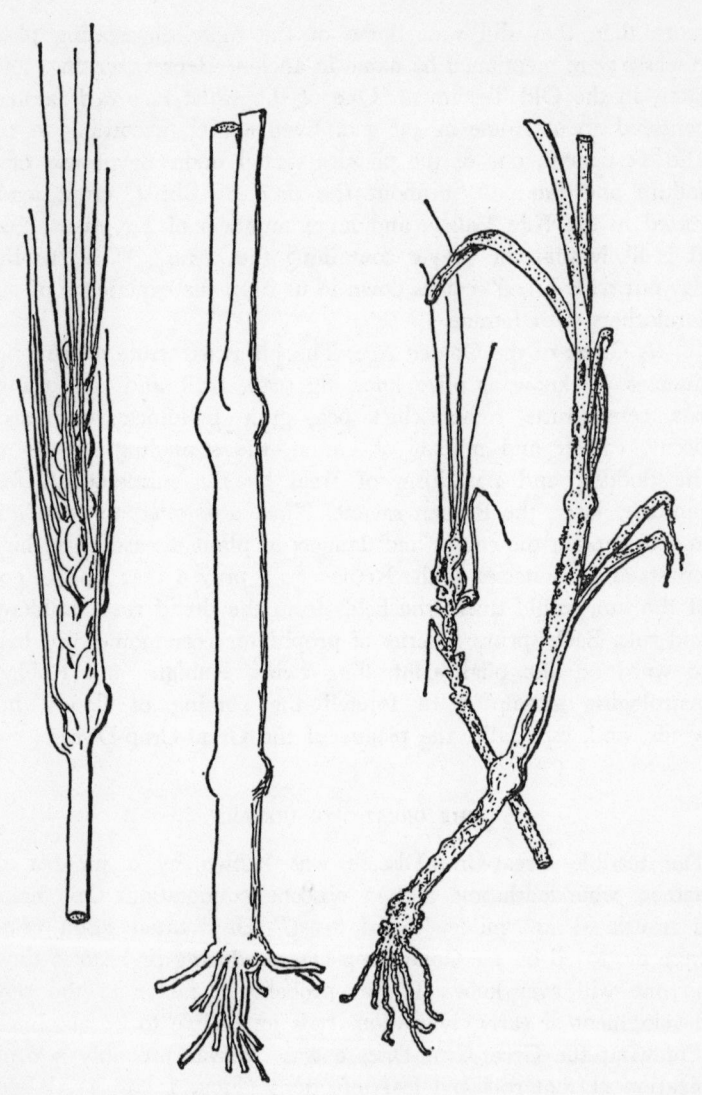

FIGURE 1 Wheat rust, caused by *Puccinia graminis tritici,* was contributory to the Great-Crop-Disease of ancient times. Severe results of attack are shown on right.

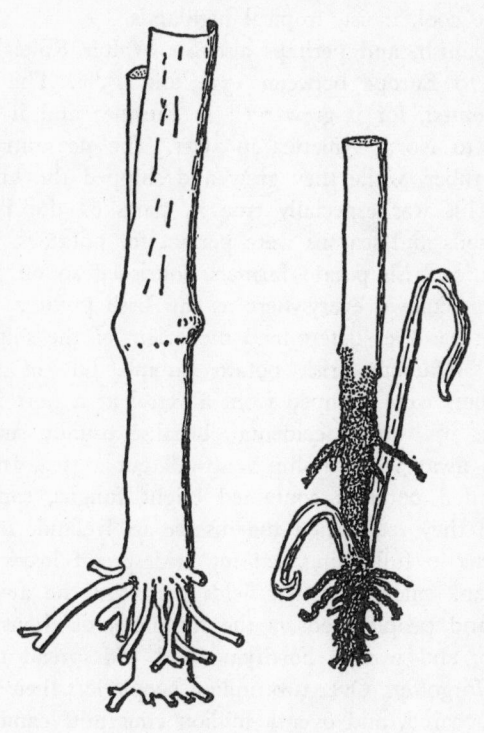

FIGURE 2 Another part of the Great-Crop-Disease was probably root rots, of which take-all, *Ophiobolus graminis*, on wheat is an example.

THE POTATO BLIGHT

Famine and death from crop blights were not peculiar to the Old World alone. Bits and pieces of information about one New World blight, the disease on potato, can be put together. The tuber of the American potato (*Solanum tuberosum*) had been planted by farmers in the tropical mountains of South America for centuries. At the same time, there was a native South American blight in potato fields caused by the fungus, *Phytophthora infestans*. Once it started, the fungus attacked with devastating vigor in the cool, moist, tropical highlands.

The Spanish, and perhaps also Sir Walter Raleigh, brought the potato to Europe between 1553 and 1588. The plant was quickly accepted, for it grew well in Europe; and it was introduced also to North America in 1621. The peasantry lived on the potato tuber, while they grew and shipped the bread grains for cash. This was especially true in parts of the British Isles where the soils and seasons were perfect for potatoes. For nearly three centuries Irish potato farmers flourished so on it that the tuber became known everywhere as the Irish potato.

No one has ever determined the origin of the shipment that started the infamous Irish potato famine, but in 1830 some diseased tubers were dumped from a vessel at a port in the Old World. This was quite accidental, because usually such rubbish was thrown away when a ship was well out at sea. In any case, these discarded potatoes contained blight fungus, some washed ashore, and they established the disease in Ireland. By 1845 an epidemic was in full swing, causing widespread losses of tubers.

The dank smell of rotten fields pervaded the air, food disappeared, and people died by the hundreds of thousands. This was famine, and was so horrifying and widespread that it has never been forgotten. Over two million people left their land, large towns disappeared, and over a million emigrants came to North America. More people left Ireland than stayed, families were driven apart, and homes were abandoned. It is fair to say that Ireland has never recovered from the pouring of its gifted, hardworking men and women into the New World.

OTHER PLANT PLAGUES

From the tenth to the nineteenth centuries, coffeegrowing and shipping were the basis for very large business enterprises in the Oriental and African tropics. Drinking coffee had become a habit and an institution, and coffeehouses were important meeting places in the Near East, Europe, and, later, the United States. The main coffee growers and shippers were Arabs, Africans,

Dutch, English, Spanish, and Portuguese. Although coffee beans came from several places, the island of Ceylon had become "coffee queen." The English in Ceylon sent coffee around the world, and, because of coffee alone, certain international banking corporations sprang up. In 1869, with coffeegrowing at its height, a very severe disease never seen before in the plantations appeared in Ceylon. At first it puzzled scientists, but they finally proved it was a rust disease caused by the fungus now called *Hemileia vastatrix*. In a few short years, this rust fungus destroyed the Ceylon plantations, causing a severe shock there which swept the world's economy like a tidal wave. Later, new planters went to the bankrupt and destroyed plantations in Ceylon where they planted tea instead and recovered some of the lost business; English merchantmen became the purveyors of that leaf, and, from that time onward, England was a nation of tea drinkers. Thus the habit of a nation was changed by a plant disease.

Another notable disease is banana wilt, or Panama disease. It is caused by root infections from the fungus *Fusarium oxysporum cubense*. In the late 1800s, large companies bought land and moved into extensive, unused tropical American regions. They cleaned up the malarial jungles and swampy river valleys; plantation companies grew bananas and developed flourishing cities, railroads, and shipping ports. Although, during their early history, the banana companies were run by foreigners independent of the Central and South American countries in which they worked, by the first part of the present century much of the vast jungle areas they had subdued changed hands and were being managed by locally trained personnel. This was soon reflected in stronger Latin American growth and prestige. About this time, epidemics of wilt came to the plantations. Regions that depended on the banana business failed, and the fears, dissatisfactions, and poverty that ensued resulted in wholesale killings, international ill will, and revolutions.

Many other crop diseases have caused vast changes in human living. For years the staple cabbages and turnips in Europe and Russia died from rotted roots caused by the clubroot fungus, *Plasmodiophora brassicae*. Losses were immense and starvation caused mass emigrations. In both the Oriental and Occidental

tropics, the rind disease of sugar cane, caused by the fungus
Melanconium sacchari, became an epidemic. In an effort to
stave off business destruction due to the fungus, a limiting factor
in those regions a century ago, sugar-cane fields were abandoned
to jungle and plantations were moved as far away as from Java
to the West Indies.

2

RUST AND ITS INFLUENCE
ON PLANT PATHOLOGY

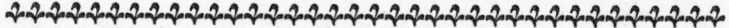

In the past, the crop plants of mankind were always in trouble. For centuries, peasants did their best with rule-of-thumb methods that reduced some losses from continually recurring plant disease. But gradually the accumulation of agricultural knowledge and increased use of scientific thinking were making themselves felt, and by the middle of the eighteenth century this science was bringing hope and then help to mankind in his war against harsh nature. Of most interest to us here is that science was being used to ease the overwhelming burden of crop diseases. This was indeed a drastic change from the blind acceptance of what was believed to be an inevitable curse and a part of the preordained course of events. This new way of thinking was a great revolutionary movement. Man at last sought to master his fate.

RUST OF WHEAT

The idea that plants might have curable diseases was early stimulated by study of the rusts of wheat. (Rust diseases of plants are caused by fungus parasites.) In 1729, Pier Antonio Micheli, botanist to the Grand Duke of Tuscany, looked at rust spots and found them to be a fungus. This was the first great move in the long battle ahead. Another unusual man, Felice Fontana of Italy, had by 1767 made further studies to determine the nature of this rust, which we now call *Puccinia graminis tritici*. Probably the most painstaking work on the disease at this time was published by Christian Hendrik Persoon (1755–1837), whose research efforts for a half century were directed towards study of wheat rust.

As is quite common in science, work like that of Persoon's writings excited interest in others. A young medical man turned botanist, Heinrich Anton deBary, became intrigued with the rust problem. Sometimes called the "Father of Plant Pathology," deBary was an amazingly effective, hard-working scientist who made superb drawings and left meticulous records of his observations. His work on the rust of wheat and other diseases not only laid the foundations for plant pathology as we know it today, but formed the basis for a good deal of our knowledge of fungi and their life cycles.

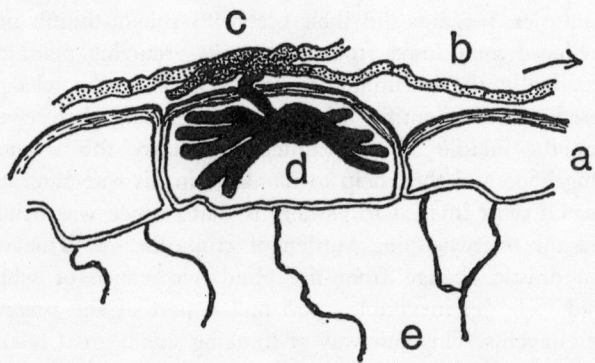

FIGURE 3 Rusts and mildews are from specialized fungi with remarkable organs called haustoria which take up host nutrients. Sketch from a highly magnified section of diseased leaf attacked by *Erysiphe graminis:* (a) leaf epidermal cell; (b) fungus growth from spore located at some distance in direction of arrow; (c) penetration of epidermal cell; (d) branched haustorium; and (e) weakened leaf cells.

Proceeding from the observations of Persoon, deBary showed how the highly specialized rust fungus first sends infection filaments, or hyphae, into the leaves of the wheat plant. He found in several fungi the minute, rounded, and wall-less structures called haustoria (Fig. 3) that actually penetrate the wheat leaf cells and serve to absorb the nutrients of the cells without killing them—a beautiful example of a delicate balance between the leaf and the fungus. Another discovery was made by deBary which, as we shall see later, had a profound impact on the thinking of pathologists. He showed that the fungus which caused this terrible rusting of wheat also caused a very different-appearing leaf spotting on the common barberry. As proof that the fungus of the barberry leaf spot and that of the wheat rust were the same, deBary took spores from the pustules on a barberry leaf and inoculated them into a wheat leaf. The spores germinated, infected the wheat plant, and produced typical rust symptoms. All this work was done prior to 1865 with equipment which was inferior to that now usually in use in grammar schools!

COMPLEX OF SPORES

During the decade 1840 to 1850, the inseparable Tulasne brothers, Louis and Charles, studied and illustrated two different-colored rust fungus spores on rusted wheat. Their observations seemed to show that the red spores and the black spores were coming from the same fungus. Not only was this confirmed by deBary but he proved experimentally that the two kinds of spores were, indeed, produced by the same fungus. He was, however, bothered by the fact that the red spores, formed in the summertime, were easy to germinate and readily caused typical wheat rust when inoculated back into healthy wheat plants, while the black spores, formed in the autumn, did not cause wheat rust when inoculated. In fact, the germination of the spores was very different. The red, summer spore formed a typical germ tube which entered the leaf, but the black spores formed a stubby, short germination tube which soon stopped growing and produced four tiny, round, transparent spores on short peg-like projections. Instead of infecting wheat, these spores could only infect the barberry plant. His work proved that the pustule produced on the barberry leaf produced yet another kind of spore which could not reinfect the barberry but did infect wheat, giving rise to typical wheat rust. Soon after the publication of these findings, deBary died.

The final step in this quite complicated and most intriguing plant disease process was not worked out for many years, not until 1927 when J. H. Craigie, in wheat-growing Western Canada, reported his finding that on the barberry there were small, almost inconspicuous pinpoint-sized lesions which contained the sexual spores of the wheat-rust fungus. Only upon sexual combination did yet another kind of spore develop, and it was this spore that caused the development of the large pustule on the barberry.

If you are slightly confused by this bizarre sequence of events, you can console yourself with the thought that many scientists were confused for a large number of years. To clarify the relation of these spore forms and types, these are given numbers. It is well to point out that there are many rusts (but not all) that have the same kind of cycle. In wheat rust, the thick-walled spore (type or stage 1) is the resting spore; on germination it produces four small spores that are the second stage or type. In wheat rust, as in some others that infect more than one kind of host, spore type 2 infects another plant, in this case the barberry bush. Small spots arise from these spore infections on a barberry leaf, and these lesions exude an insect-attractant of honey-like drops in which are the tiny spores of type 3. These spores are mixed, by insect feeding or other means, and the tiny spores fuse. The fusion cell develops inside the barberry leaf and causes a growth that thrusts forth the so-called cups in which are found the large spores of stage or type 4. (To repeat, when the rust goes from wheat to barberry, spores of type 2 are the means of infecting the barberry leaves, and spores of type 3 and type 4 develop on the bush.) Spores of type 4 from barberry infect wheat to produce the summer spores, type 5. As the summer season progresses, in the same lesion there develop, along with spore type 5, the so-called winter or resting spores of type 1. The early formed summer spores, type 5, cause added wheat rust. It is renewed cycles of these summer spores released into the air to infect other wheat plants that bring about rust epidemics in wheat.

THE STAFF OF LIFE

Although the elucidation of the different phases of parasitism of the wheat rust was an intellectually satisfying experience for the mycologists (specialists in the fungi) and the plant pathologists who worked with them, the findings were of greatest importance in their practical applications for farmers concerned with the health of their crops. With the establishment of the fact that the rust overwinters mainly (but not exclusively) in the form of black spores which can only infect barberry, farmers learned that the eradication of barberry plants near wheat fields reduced the chances of wheat rust the following spring. And even some reduction in the severity of the disease helped, because wheat was the primary cereal grain of Western man; the bread he made from it was the staff of life for millions of people in Europe, North America, the Middle East, and the northern part of Asia. If the wheat crop failed, people could, in some cases, turn to barley and rye; but when rusts, bunts, smuts, leaf blights, root rots, and mildews attacked these other grains, famine was not far behind.

DISEASE RESISTANCE

Though removal of the barberry helped, much better help was on the way. Some years before 1900, agricultural specialists in the United States Government were trying various means to control the devastations from wheat rust. Changing of fertilizers, seeding methods, and moving crops to other fields were unsuccessful. Then B. T. Galloway discovered that he could grow rust-free wheat by spraying the plants with a fungicide, though he also found this was hard work and economically prohibitive. A colleague, M. A. Carleton, had been studying rust disease on wheat plots from seeds he was securing from all over the world. Most of his test plants showed severe rust, except for two varieties that came from Russia. These wheats proved to be practically immune to rust, and

Carleton decided to use them as rust-resistant parents for breeding purposes. The result was a strain of wheat grown in America which farmers could plant with little fear of rust attack.

SUBSPECIES AND RACES OF CEREAL RUSTS

One of the great landmarks in the history of plant pathology was a classic study (1894) on the cereal rusts by Professor Jakob Eriksson of Sweden. He was interested in the grain crops attacked by rust, and he found hitherto unsuspected differences among the rusts. It was plain that wheat rust, *Puccinia graminis,* developed only on wheat. Wheat-rust spores inoculated onto oats caused no disease, although oat-rust spores placed on oats caused rust. Likewise oat rust inoculated onto wheat caused no wheat rust. Eriksson found marked specificity with several other rusts on their particular hosts. It was impossible for anyone to tell the rusts one from another by examining spores under a microscope—they were all known as *Puccinia graminis.* But when Eriksson finished his cross-inoculation experiments, he found that though the spores of many cereal rusts looked the same, or were morphologically identical, they were pathologically different, for they attacked only certain hosts, and so he gave them special names to indicate this. The wheat rust is now designated as the subspecies *Puccinia graminis tritici,* oat rust is *Puccinia graminis avenae,* the one on rye *Puccinia graminis secalis,* and so on.

More than twenty years later, Elvin C. Stakman, a young native of Wisconsin, discovered that the subspecies wheat rust could be broken down even further. He collected spores from wheat fields attacked by *Puccinia graminis tritici* in Minnesota and other wheat-growing states. On inoculating wheats with the various rust collections and growing them side by side, he discovered he had physiologically different wheat rust races; some collections caused disease in a variety of wheat that other rusts didn't injure.

By 1914, Stakman published his now classic paper, "A Study in Cereal Rusts: Physiological Races," giving the proof for the physiological differences that allowed him to designate separate races of wheat rust. After this report came out, pathologists working with other crop diseases learned that many parasitic fungi also are composed of physiological and pathological races. It is now known that new races appear by mutation, and the fact that a fungus species is readily mutable is a matter of great economic importance.

Let us consider a variety or strain of a crop that has been bred for resistance to its most serious disease. The successful variety becomes well fixed in its resistance character, is accepted by farmers and consumers, and used all over the world. Year after year billions upon billions of spores from the old disease batter at the resistant plants; at first, gratifyingly, without success. One spring, a spore develops that is genetically different from the other billions of spores. It happens to land on a normally resistant plant, but, because of some new mutant characteristic, the spore is able to infect the plant. Successful at last, the disease prospers on this first plant and lives to send off new spores, all with the mutant characteristic which proved so useful. These spores infect the so-called resistant crop and thereby cause disease that spreads widely and rapidly. Thus, the old disease has survived by changing its characteristics.

The appearance of a new, more infective race of a parasite means that a formerly resistant crop is suddenly threatened everywhere it is grown. The whole job of obtaining resistance starts all over again.

SECURING RESISTANCE BY EXPLORING FOR PLANTS

Though one of man's most effective plant disease controls is the growing of resistant varieties, securing resistant parents is not easy. It requires a careful search and often extensive travel to secure such plants. Some of the most scrubby, primitive, and unattractive types are tough and remarkably disease-resistant. These original types of plants are supremely important to a nationwide or even world-wise agricultural industry. Often the original wild plants still have genes for disease resistance that were unwittingly lost through many centuries of selection for varieties of high quality, larger size, better looks, or more productivity.

Thus, an activity not always thought of as part of plant-dis-

ease study, but of vital importance to it, is that of plant exploration. In whatever country one finds oneself, either as grower or
scientist, one becomes impressed with the fact that many times
the important crops about him all seem to have originated somewhere else than the fields in which they grow.

Over the years, important diseases have been carried with
crops from their countries of origin. If the crop is not too in-
tensively grown, it may temporarily escape the worst disease effects, producing sufficiently for good economic gain. However, as
fields become larger, closer together, and replanted more often, and
as crop varieties are selected and reselected for horticultural uni-
formity and quality, the diseases build up, making greater and
greater inroads on yield. In some instances this build-up can be
so dangerous that famine threatens. It is precisely at this time,
when disease control becomes the most difficult, that the scientist
has to go back to the place where the plant species originated.
There, sometimes in the most romantic and at the same time the
most uncomfortable of surroundings, he may discover old types
and wild varieties of his special crop plant that have successfully
resisted the disease for thousands of years. Certain individuals
have been more resistant to natural disease and have thus been
able to live on where others died. These resistant crop strains
may be the answer for the farmers faced with the extermination
of their disease-threatened plants.

There are many instances of the use of resistant plant types.
For elm trees resistant to the Dutch elm disease (*Ceratostomella
ulmi*), workers in the United States have planted resistant selections from Holland. The blueberry is plagued with a serious stem
canker (*Physalospora corticis*), and resistance to it was found in
North Carolina in plants where the canker persists in wild stands.
In the devastating anthracnose (*Colletotrichum graminicola*) of
grain sorghum, selections made in Africa where the grain and the
disease are both native have resulted in highly resistant types. Celery came from Asia Minor and its two most important leaf blights
(*Cercospora apii* and *Septoria apii-graveolentis*) can be eliminated
by breeding varieties using genes from celery strains secured from
Turkey, where the diseases and the vegetable have been long together. Cabbage yellows (*Fusarium oxysporum conglutinans*) re-

sistance is found in selections of the plant brought from its original home on the chalk cliffs of England. Resistance to diseases of pepper has been found in varieties from its homeland areas of New Mexico, Mexico, and Peru. Disease resistance may not in every case be the only control, but where applicable there is nothing as effective.

3

SIMPLEST PLANT-DISEASE ORGANISMS

Most plant diseases are the result of infections or parasitism by microorganisms. The plant that is infected is called the "host," and the organisms that attack them can be grouped into six great categories: nematodes, algae, fungi, yeasts, bacteria, and viruses.

For any one of these kinds of parasites to succeed, the most important factor is that it reach its victim; in this regard, small size and large numbers are vital considerations. With innumerable natural hazards to overcome, it is an advantage if there is a superabundance of individuals, for this reduces the likelihood of some outside factor eliminating an entire species of attacking parasite. And superabundant numbers are more efficiently produced if the individuals are small, for it takes less protoplasm for each organism.

Another advantage to small size is that there is much more surface in relation to the organism's weight. If dry and loosened from any support, the very small organism can be more readily lifted into the air. Once in the air, breezes take the microscopic spores farther; fungus spores have been found two or three miles above the earth, and can be carried for many hundreds of miles.

BACTERIA IN PLANTS

It has been only a little more than a century since men first
realized that innocent-looking air carried fungi and bacteria. And
it was a long time after Pasteur's classic proofs that airborne
bacteria caused the contamination of wounds in men and animals
that it became known that bacteria also infected plants. There
are about 170 species of bacteria that cause plant diseases, and
they attack an even larger number of hosts.

For many years, the pathologist believed that even if bacteria
infected animals or men they could be disregarded as possible disease producers in plants, because it was believed that all disease-
causing bacteria in animals developed in the blood, and in the
laboratory it was known they grew best in warm incubators. Plant
sap is cool, and is chemically and biologically much different from
blood. Plant sap is carried in closed tissues; it is passed from cell
to cell in a quite different manner than is the free-flowing blood
in the veins of animals. It was therefore difficult to conceive of
bacteria moving inside plants the way they did in animals.

In the 1890s, Thomas J. Burrill, a young professor of botany at
the University of Illinois, was called upon to help fruit growers
with a baffling disease problem. Although the particular disease
was present in other states, it had become increasingly severe in
the Illinois fruit region, where it was killing thousands of trees.
It was not caused by insects, and fungi could not be incriminated.
From the killed and blackened shoots and flowers of the apple
tree (Fig. 4), Burrill isolated a bacterium, and was able to grow
it as pure cultures by using methods employed for studying animal
and human bacterial pathogens. He carried his cultures through
many studies, inoculated and reinoculated fruit trees with bacterium, and found that it caused typical pear and apple blight.
Today, this organism, now called *Erwinia amylovora,* is recognized in many parts of the world.

Burrill was the first to establish and describe the presence
of any bacterium capable of causing disease in plants. Others
confirmed his findings and also discovered different kinds of
plants killed by other bacteria. Many authorities continued to

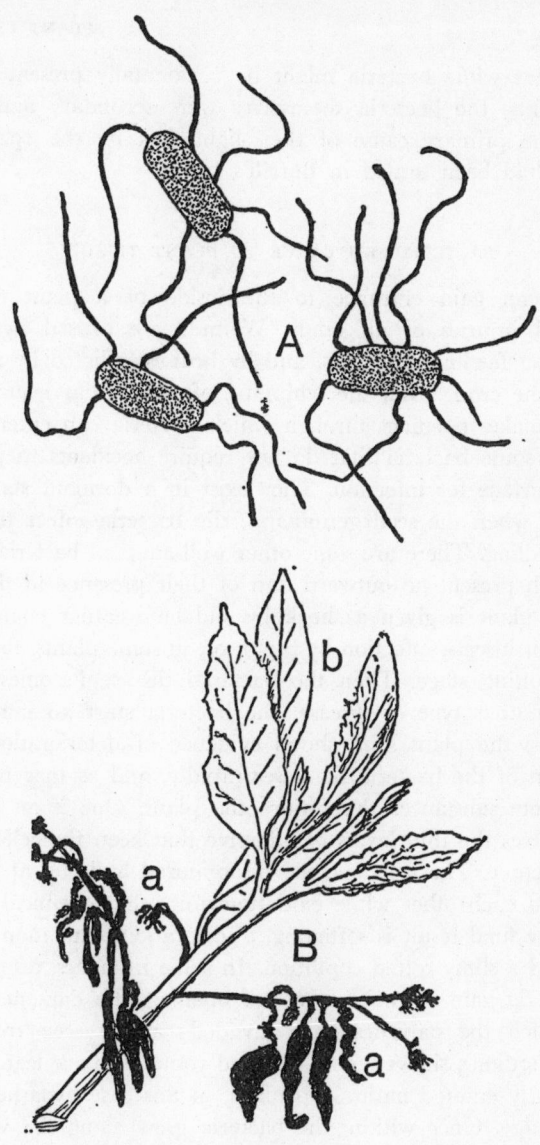

FIGURE 4 Apple fire-blight disease, *Erwinia amylovora*. A. Drawing of highly magnified bacteria showing flagellae. B. Small apple tree branch with: (a) blighted twigs originally infected through flowers; (b) uninfected twig.

believe that while bacteria might be accidentally present in diseased plants, the bacteria themselves were secondary and could not be the primary cause of the blight, but by the 1920s, the question had been settled in Burrill's favor.

BACTERIAL ENTRANCE TO PLANT TISSUE

Bacteria can gain entrance to the inside of a plant through accidental injuries of all kinds. Wounds are caused by blown sand, insect feeding, and cuts, and by bruises inflicted by man in growing the crop. Even the whipping of winds that beats leaves together makes openings through which bacteria can enter. Then there are some bacteria that do not require accidents to prepare a plant surface for infection. They exist in a dormant state in a seed, and when the seed germinates, the bacteria infect the very young seedling. There are some other well-adapted bacterial parasites which present no outward sign of their presence in the host until the plant is given a shock by sudden weather change, infestation of insects, infection by fungi, or, in some plants, the onset of the fruiting stage. Then the bacterial disease becomes acute.

In another type of disease, the bacteria start an immediate attack and the plant soon shows evidence of deterioration. The population of the bacteria increases rapidly, and as they multiply they excrete substances that injure the plant. One is an enzyme that dissolves the thin layers of adhesive that keep the cells firmly stuck together. The cells become disorganized and slip apart and away from each other while oxidation and other chemical effects occur. The final result is softening, discoloration, exudation of cell juices, and a slimy rotted condition. In some instances, after parasitic bacteria gain entrance to a leaf opening, the darkened veins down which the parasites have invaded can be seen from the outside. FIGURE 5 shows such a diseased young cabbage leaf. Bacteria evidently entered natural openings, in this case hydathodes on the leaf edge. Once within, the bacteria grew along the vascular tissues through the small netted veins to the larger veins, then down the petiole which leads into the main part of the plant.

Certain bacteria stimulate plant cells into excessive multiplication, which results in swellings, galls, and tumors. These enlarge-

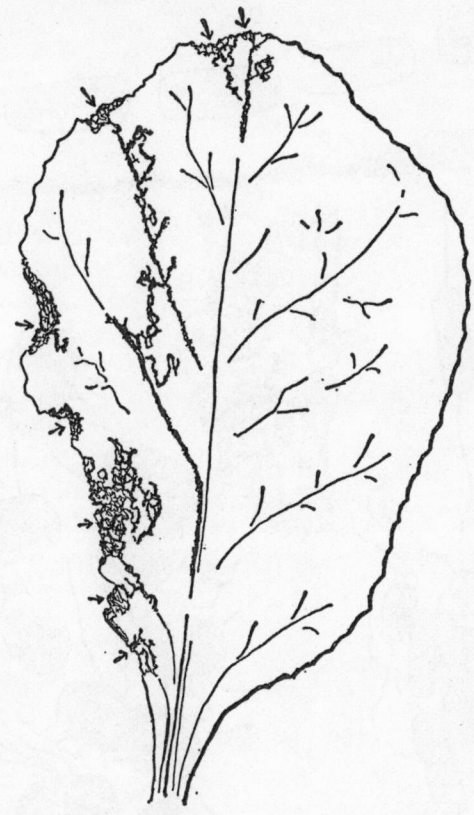

FIGURE 5 Young leaf of cabbage diseased with bacterial black rot, *Xanthomonas campestris*. Infections occurred (arrows) in hydathodes inoculated with pure culture. Disease followed veinlets to larger veins and spread through them into rest of plant.

ments sometimes become infected with other organisms. Thus, in addition to direct dislocation of sap-carrying plant parts, the disease is augmented by added infections. One bacterial wilt disease, caused by *Pseudomonas solanacearum*, affects plants both by killing cells with poisonous substances excreted by the parasite

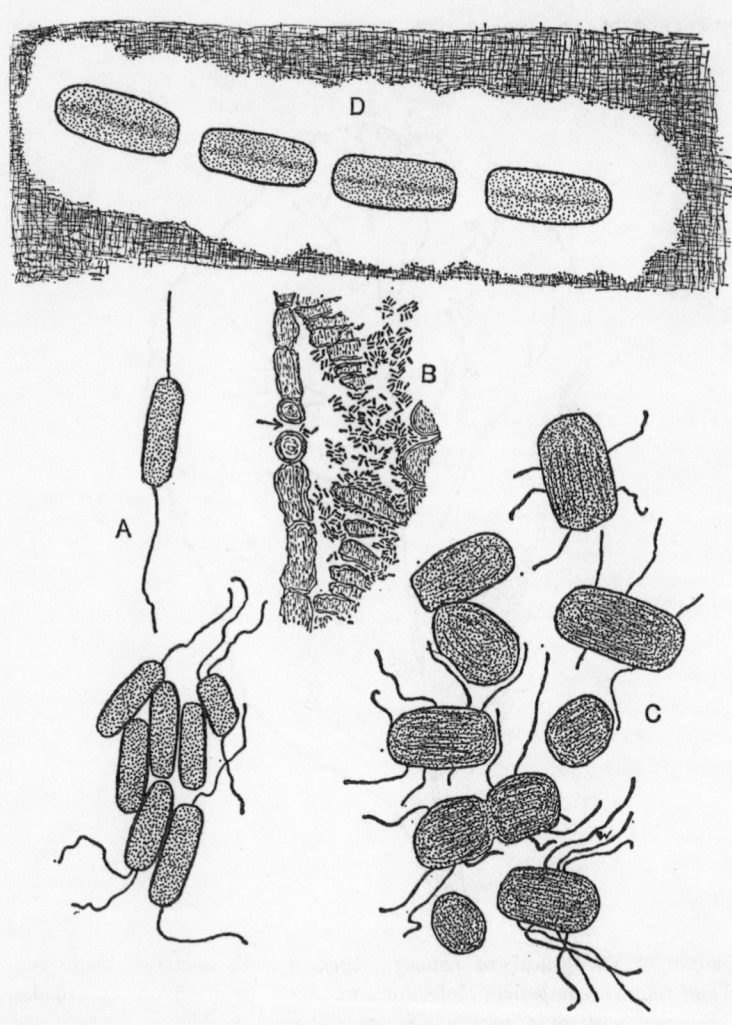

FIGURE 6 Examples of a few plant disease bacteria, drawn under high miscroscopic magnification. A. Shape and appendages of *Xanthomonas campestries*, cause of cabbage black rot. B. Bean leaf cross section infected through stomate (arrow) by *Xanthomonas phaseoli*. C. Individual bacteria, one dividing, of *Erwinia carotovora*, which cause soft rot in very many products. D. incapsulated bacteria, *Erwinia tracheiphila*, in a smear from wilted, dying cucumber plant.

and, because so many organisms are present, by clogging the xylem vessels.

Since plant-disease bacteria are grown so easily in the laboratory, they readily lend themselves to study (Fig. 6). They differ from one another in many ways: in morphology; in the temperatures at which they grow best; in the fact that some can move by themselves while others cannot; in what nutrients will maintain them; and in their susceptibility to different disinfectants.

PARASITIC ALGAE AND YEASTS

While most algae—such as the green growth one commonly sees on moist sides of trees and rocks, or those large branched colonies of algal cells that are called seaweed—are harmless, some species of algae cause diseases in crop plants. Most of these troublesome forms are found in the tropics.

The most important parasitic alga is *Cephaleuros virescens,* best known in moist tropical countries, although it occurs at times as far north into the Temperate Zone as North Carolina. *C. virescens* infects a long list of crop plants and the leaves of jungle trees, causing spots, blotches, breaks in the bark, malformations and constrictions on foliage, fruits, and stems. It also causes severe and untimely defoliation that can weaken both small plants and large trees, making them more susceptible to disease from other less virulent parasitic fungi or bacteria.

It is well known that certain algae (Fig. 7) combine with certain fungi in symbiotic, mutually valuable relationships and form lichens. Certain of the lichens, one genus of which is called *Strigula,* develop into a white growth, appearing as usually harmless leaf and stem spots. In rare instances in the tropics, however, the white lichen is so luxurious in its smothering development that it damages leaves on which neither the fungus nor the alga partner of the lichen will cause any disease.

Algae, as plant parasites, are splashed about in dew and rain and require conditions of warmth and the presence of water on host surfaces. This results in bursting of the small globular sac, or sporangium, at the tip of a slender filament of the alga. Inside the sporangium are microscopic, naked spores that escape or

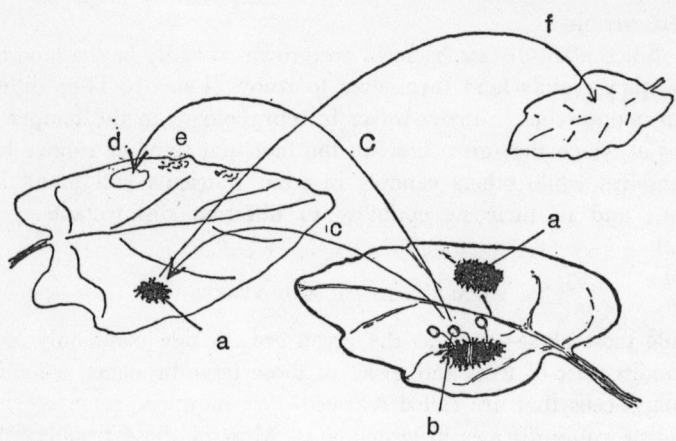

FIGURE 7 Diagram of: (a) the parasitic alga, *Cephaleuros virescens;* sporangia (b) open in water to let loose free swimming spores that are then splashed (c) to other leaves, where they sometimes (d) become a lichen, *Strigula* sp., by combined growth with (e) a fungus. Water-drop spread (f) often covers long distance "steps."

swarm out of the burst sac and swim away. For their size, they move rapidly and for quite a distance.

PLANT PARASITIZING YEASTS

There is another small group of unique plant parasitic microorganisms, the yeasts. Yeasts are most commonly associated with the leavening process in breadmaking, in fermenting wines, in other fermenting actions, and in the commercial production of certain organic chemicals. Fungus specialists, or mycologists, include yeasts with the fungi. However, it is convenient for us to consider them separately.

Yeast rots are common in ripening fruits and occasionally increase the severity of rots in vegetables started by other microorganisms. Indeed, yeast rots are so common that consumers at times have been warned against them. During the prohibition era in the United States, producers of canned and bottled fruit juices were known to label the containers with distinct admonitions that there should be no emptying of the containers into a crock in a warm location and then allowing "in careless manner" ripened fruits to fall into the juice. If this happened and it was then covered and allowed to stand, the result would be "dangerous," as any sterile juice so treated would without doubt be contaminated by wild yeasts. With aging it might make a good wine, and this was certainly not the purpose of the juice purveyors!

The most remarkable of the truly parasitic yeasts belong to the genus *Nematospora* and are found in many parts of the world. Spores of the parasites are sticky and are distributed by being carried on puncturing and feeding mouth parts of a number of the true stink bugs, the Pentatomids. These insects, with their contaminated beaks, probe deeply into fruits to suck juices from seeds. In doing so they leave infecting yeasts, resulting in seed diseases like the seed spotting and collapse in dry lima beans and cowpeas, or the stripe, or zebra, blemish of coffee. *Nematospora* infects seed and discolors lint in the cotton bolls, and one species of it causes death of seeds and breakdown of pulp in grapefruit.

4

VIRUS INFECTIONS

There are a large number of viruses that attack hundreds of kinds of crop plants in the Temperate Zone and tropics. Effects of virus infections range from benign, as in potato latent virus, in which no symptoms are seen on the plant, through all kinds of intermediate infections, to severe injuries, and finally to those causing collapse and death. An example of the latter is the elm phloem necrosis marked by dark streaks in the wood followed by a period of decline and ending in the death of the entire tree. Distinct crippling witches' brooming, or twisted growth are the characteristic signs of many virus-diseased plants. A suggestion of mottling and malformation from virus disease on leaves is shown in FIGURE 8. When juices are squeezed from such leaves and rubbed on healthy plants, often the first effect of virus infection is the appearance of local lesions. After the virus enters, it may go through the plant (systemic infection), causing stunt, mottling, or other effects.

The best-known leaf symptom of a virus disease is mosaic. There is unusual spotting along and about veins, green and yellow markings in islands and streaks, and often brown stippling and dark lines between spots. The word "mosaic" of course refers to the almost decorative appearance of an affected leaf. The patterning suggests the ancient method of making a design or picture

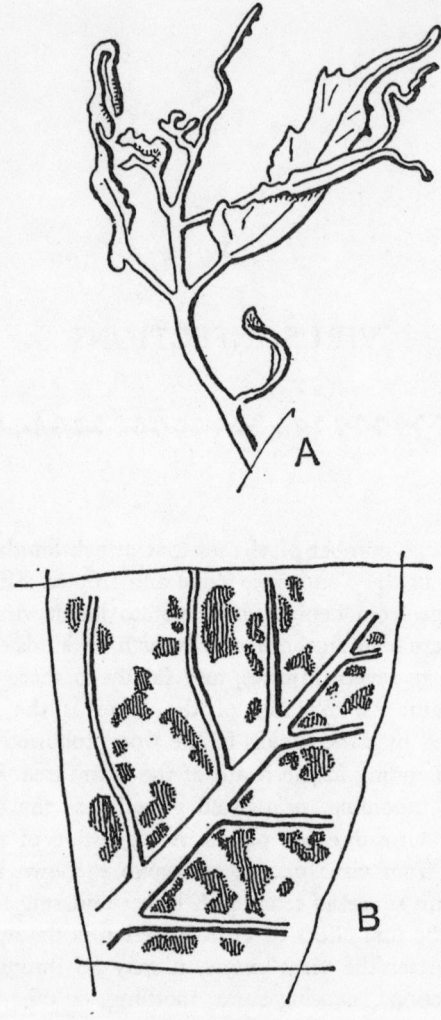

FIGURE 8 Certain virus disease symptoms: A. Fern leaf and twist of tomato from cucumber virus. B. Mottle pattern on tobacco leaf from common mosaic.

by skillfully setting small, variously colored bits of stone, marble, and pieces of glazed ceramic in a cement matrix.

DISCOVERY OF PLANT MOSAIC

Of the great many mosaic diseases of plants, the first one to be studied carefully was the spectacular disease that spoiled tobacco leaves. During the middle of the nineteenth century there were occasional reports of that new tobacco leaf disturbance. It was found in various parts of the world, but it was the source of most curiosity in Europe. In the beginning only a few farmers saw this on tobacco, but in less than a decade it became more severe and some fields were total losses. The growers in Holland were the worst hit. It was especially critical for them, as they produced handsome, fragrant tobacco leaves for the best cigars. The plants raised by the Dutch East Indies plantations, which sent the finest wrapper leaves obtainable to factories in Holland, also had the disease.

In 1870 a deputation of Dutch farmers went to their government, and Adolph Mayer, then head of the Agricultural Experiment Station, became intrigued with the problem. At first he felt it might be a bacterium, which was remarkable thinking, because in those days plant disease-causing bacteria were not usually believed possible. He found that, in a field, the disease appeared first in only a few plants and then one plant began to catch it from another. Repeated attempts to isolate the cause convinced him that no fungus was involved. Even after many tests Mayer was unable to incriminate a bacterium (and no one in those days expected he would). But using controlled conditions, he managed to spread the disease from one plant to another by applying the juice from diseased leaves to healthy plants. He finally concluded that the plants were affected by neither fungus nor bacterium, but by something like an enzyme. In his description of the disease in 1885 he called the symptoms "a mosaic of spots." The name mosaic has been used for it and similar diseases ever since.

The news of Mayer's report was received with interest in various institutions. Pathologists were skeptical that fungi were not involved, and there was some feeling the disease might be partially caused by poor fertilizing practices. The Russian scientist Demetri Ivanowski of St. Petersburg decided to carry research on the infective juices a step further than had been done in Holland. He passed the sap from diseased leaves through a porcelain filter that successfully retained all fungi or bacteria. Using this filtered juice for inoculation purposes, he produced mosaic on healthy tobacco plants. He believed those filtered drops contained a special agent, which he spoke of as a *contagium vivum fluidum* (a contagious living fluid). This *contagium* he called "virus."

By the close of the nineteenth century there had been only a moderate amount of study on plant viruses. However, it was sufficient to open up new explanations and new approaches to diseases of hitherto unknown causes. Viral diseases, it was found, were common enough in plants to be of enormous economic concern. And with each discovery, the true nature of virus became more important.

NATURE OF VIRUS

In 1935 a great plant-virus finding stirred the whole scientific world. W. M. Stanley, who was later awarded a Nobel prize for his work, announced that by chemical means he had precipitated the tobacco mosaic virus as crystals. Stanley considered he had —in the purified condition—an inert chemical, not something living. The dry virus crystals are long, light-colored needles with a silky sheen that dissolves in water. Using an aqueous solution, Stanley infected healthy tobacco plants with the mosaic. This crystallization, indicating a complex chemical nature, was one of the greatest steps forward in all virus study.

At about this time electronic theory was progressing to the point that engineers and others could start designing instruments to study ultra-small-sized particles. Between 1924 and 1932, physicists were following the courses, or trajectories, of electrons in electrostatic lenses. Physicists and biologists found the possibilities exciting, and by 1939 ways had been devised to photograph figures, called micrographs, of opaque structures and forms that held electrons back. Of most benefit to plant pathologists, a way was found to do this with virus particles. For the first time, scientists could see outlines of things they had long known were there but which were much too small to be demonstrated in any conventional microscope. Electron microscopes were in common use by 1946, and it was possible to observe viruses regularly. Electron microscope photographs of virus particles are used to obtain measurements, determine shapes, find where particles are in tissues, and help diagnose the kind of virus present.

A great deal has been learned since 1946 about the nature of a virus. Fundamental studies about the classic tobacco mosaic virus have been a very useful source of knowledge about the nature of viruses generally, whether in plants, animals, or men. From electron microscopy it was found that tobacco virus particles are in the shape of medium-long rods. The rods measure about 300 millimicrons long by 15 thick (a millimicron is $\frac{1}{1,000,000}$ of one millimeter). Electron micrographs have been taken of numerous plant viruses, and the differences in shape are interesting. Some of the range in variation is indicated in FIGURE 9.

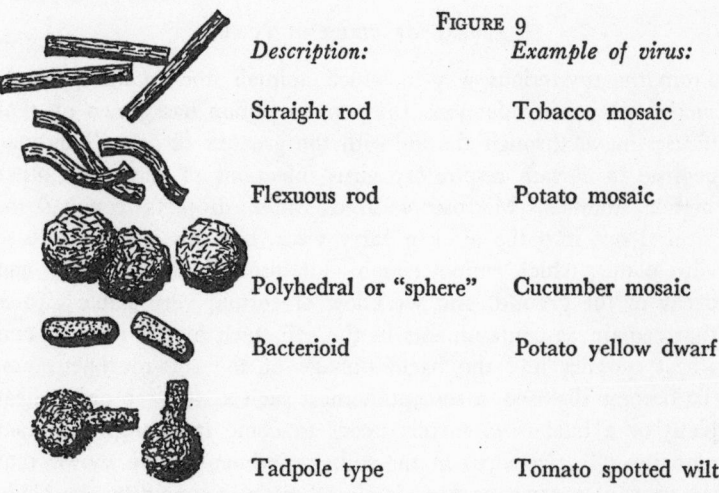

FIGURE 9

Description:	Example of virus:
Straight rod	Tobacco mosaic
Flexuous rod	Potato mosaic
Polyhedral or "sphere"	Cucumber mosaic
Bacterioid	Potato yellow dwarf
Tadpole type	Tomato spotted wilt

Many chemical studies show there is a nucleic acid core in virus particles. In the particles of such widely different viruses as tobacco mosaic and human influenza, the core is RNA, or ribonucleic acid. Another point of interest is that the core is not naked but is encased with protein. If virus particles are in the shape of rods, the tube-like sheathing is of slender elongated protein filaments bound together side by side to make the tube. If particles are "spheres," or of the sphere-like polyhedral shape, the outside protein covering is in the form of a shell.

It has been amply proven that viruses increase within host tissues. Variations in viruses arise that are manifested by host disease reactions. These variations can be carried on by transfer of the disease to healthy hosts which will succumb to disease of the new type. These seem simple statements, but are important because these characteristics of growth, reproduction, and variation are true of all living things. One criticism of the idea that viruses are alive is that viruses cannot multiply by themselves. But this is also true of many parasites. In nature, certain bacteria and some nematodes are specifically dependent on a particular host. There are certain fungi and also certain mistletoes that cannot exist without their specific hosts.

SPREAD OF VIRUS IN FIELDS

From the mysterious way in which animals and plants suddenly succumb to virus infections, the popular notion has grown up that viruses move through the air with the greatest of ease. This may be true in certain respiratory virus infections of man and other higher animals. Microscopic-sized water droplets coughed or sneezed out into the air can carry virus, but this is not the case with plants, which cannot cough. But diseased plants do die and decay in the ground, and we know of certain very stable viruses that remain as contaminants in the soil, such as the tobacco and wheat mosaics and the bacteriophage of the soft-rot bacterium. To become diseased, a susceptible host such as tobacco or a wheat plant or a bacterium merely needs to come into proper contact with the effective virus in the soil. Experiments have shown that the virus of sugar-cane stunt is almost entirely spread by the blade of the cane-cutting knife employed in harvest. In the case of a few viruses, such as tobacco mosaic in tobacco or the southern celery mosaic in tomato, very little is required to distribute them. Many times the touch of a finger tip on a diseased leaf and then

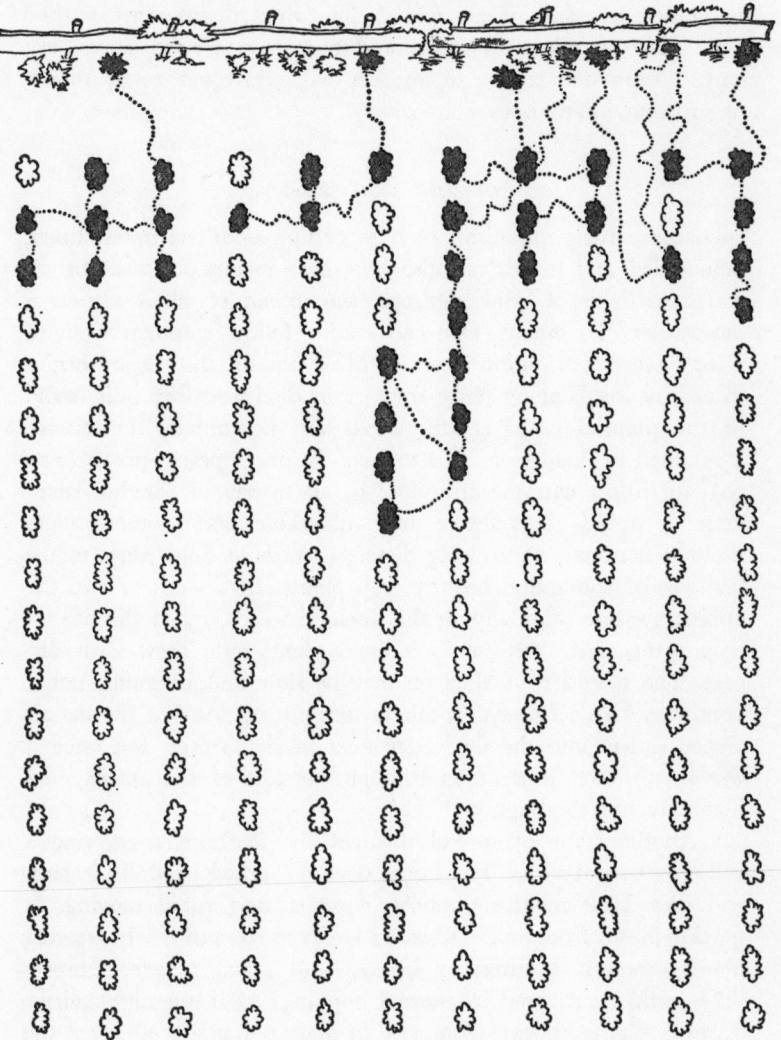

FIGURE 10 Diagram to represent slow southern celery mosaic spread in the field; diseased plants indicated in black (weeds along fence, crop in field rows) and movement of crawling insect, *Aphis* sp., shown by dotted lines.

on a healthy plant is enough. A few virus diseases are carried from place to place in seeds, and numerous viruses have been spread from one region to another when infected roots, tubers, or growing plants have been moved.

INSECTS AND VIRUSES

In nature, living organisms such as certain dodders, mites, fungi, nematodes, and insects are also known as means of spreading viruses. In fields of growing crops, the spread of plant viruses is mostly done by insects. One can readily follow common types of virus disease distribution in crops. Most usually, the disease begins in nearby weeds along fence rows or in ditches before it is found in the planted crop. If the weeds are perennials, the disease is retained in them from year to year. In one type of spread (FIG. 10), an insect carrying the virus is, let us say, a wingless plant louse or aphid. This feeble and vulnerable plant louse bridges the gap between the growing diseased weeds at field edges to the first row of young and healthy crop plants. In a week or two the aphids, feeding originally on the diseased weeds, reach the nearest crop plants, and these newly infested plants soon show virus disease. The spread from then on may be slow and irregular, but it continues with certainty. As one farmer put it, "At first the mosaic seeped slowly into the field edge next to sick weeds, but once it was in my crop it went on through the rest of the acreage deliberately but thoroughly."

Another type of spread involves the leafhopper carrying a yellows or stunt virus. The insect does not crawl or walk, it hops and flies. It is relatively robust, nervous, and rapid moving. It quickly jumps from tough, diseased weeds to rows of newly growing plants. Soon it is lifted by breezes and taken longer distances than could be covered by normal hopping. As if overnight, virus-diseased plants appear (FIG. 11) in scattered places all over the field. Here and there these hoppers have visited, fed a little, spread by skipping from plant to plant, gone rapidly from row to row. It was after seeing such a spread that an overworked farmer, with pardonable exaggeration, said, "The virus swept through, like fire driven by the wind."

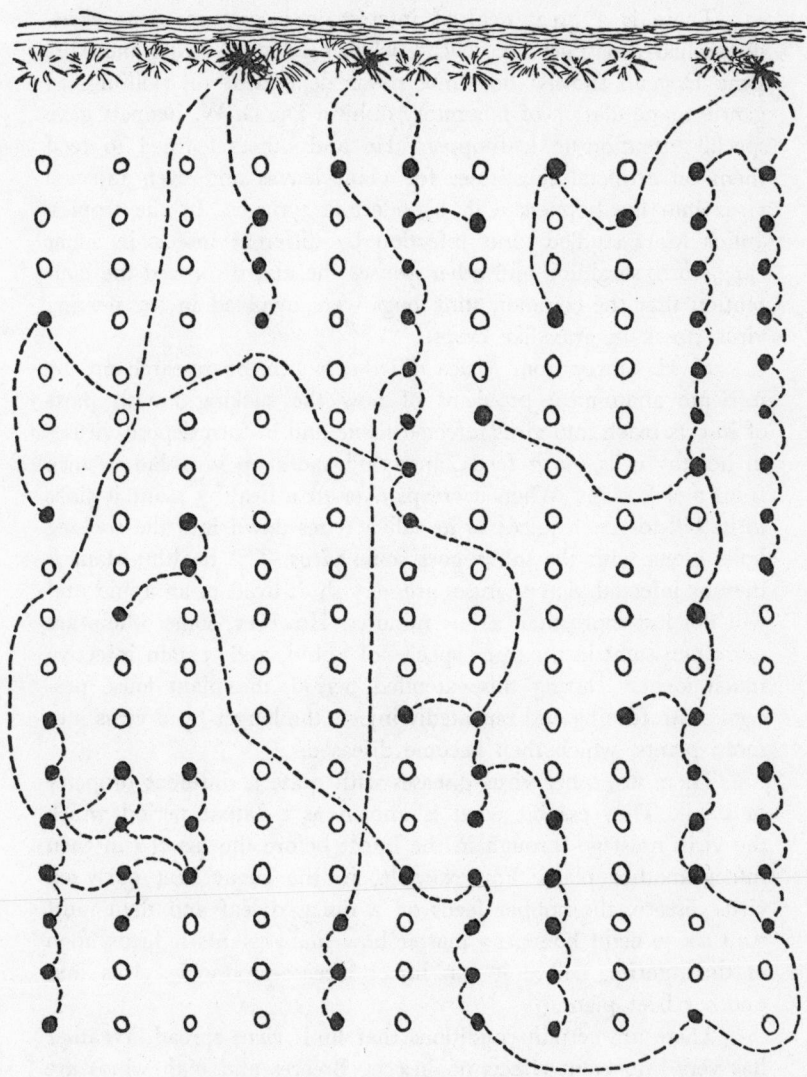

FIGURE 11 Diagram to represent fast corn stunt virus spread in the field; diseased plants indicated in black (weed grasses and volunteer corn along roadway, crop in field rows) and movement of hopping or flying insect, *Dalbulus* sp., shown by dashed lines.

There is a great deal of interest in insects as plant virus-disease carriers. They are delicate when held in captivity, and Miss Isme Hoggan showed how much was dependent on skillful and gentle manipulation of laboratory aphids. Dr. C. W. Bennett gave special attention to leafhoppers. He and others learned to feed them on artificial substitutes for plant leaves and even injected virus into the hoppers with hypodermic syringes. In the tropics, Julius Matz studied virus infection by different insects in sugar cane, corn, sorghum, and other grasses; he also disproved the contention that the common stink bugs were involved in transferring virus streak in grass-like crops.

H. H. Storey from Africa did the pioneering research on the intricate anatomical problems of how the sucking mouth parts of insects reach into virus infected tissue and in turn deposit viruses in healthy cells. As it feeds, an aphid sucks up virus-laden juice from a sick plant. When it creeps over to a healthy plant it sinks in its bill for fresh juice; as its saliva oozes down into the sucking hole, along with the saliva goes some virus. The healthy plant is thereby infected. Some viruses are very short-lived in an aphid and will not last more than a few minutes. However, some others are more persistent in the same species of aphid, and remain infective much longer. During this extended period, the plant louse proceeds with feeding and repeatedly injects the longer-lived virus into more plants, which then become diseased.

There are other virus diseases with quite a different property or habit. They exhibit what is known as a latent period which the virus must go through in the insect before the insect can then infect another plant. For example, in the sugar beet curly-top virus disease, the hopper feeds on a diseased leaf and then must wait six to eight hours, no matter how many plants it feeds upon in the interim, before it can inject disease-producing virus into another beet plant.

There are certain conditions that limit virus spread. Weather has very important effects on insects. Breezes and high winds are responsible for carrying winged aphids, leafhoppers, whiteflies, and other sucking insects to places where they might not otherwise go. An unexpected heat wave or an unusual cold spell holds down movement of insects until normal weather returns. In the Temperate Zone, viruses do not move until plant growth begins in the spring. However, even where growth never ceases in the tropics, if there are long and hard beating rains they tear up and kill insects, and in some tropical rain-forest regions, virus-carrying sucking insects cannot survive. There, without the insect carriers, viruses are no great problem. But in parts of the tropics outside rain-battered areas, where there is no checking of insects, movement of virus never stops.

VIRUS CONTROL IN THE FIELD

Reduction in numbers of virus disease-carrying insects, even without absolutely complete kill, is often sufficient to allow commercially feasible control of a mosaic or other virus disease. When the plant pathologist determines which weeds harbor the virus and what insects carry it, he advises the grower that control may be attacked from two angles: Either the wild plants that are sources of virus can be killed by mechanical or herbicidal means, or insecticides and other measures can be used to reduce numbers of sucking leafhoppers, plant lice, or other insects that carry the virus.

Of course, the most ideal control of all is resistance in the crops themselves. There are many varieties of crops that are virus-resistant. Using resistant varieties, growers of sugar beets, beans, and numerous other plants can once again produce crops in fields from which they were driven off because of viruses. A classic example of this is the resistant POJ (the letters standing for the name of the Dutch experiment stations working on sugar cane in the Dutch East Indies) sugar canes from Java. These resistant varieties gave a crop which, in spite of sugar-cane mosaic virus, produced sugar not only in the tropics of the Orient and of Africa, but also in the Americas. It is impossible to estimate how much the scientists of the old Dutch East Indies helped the world by breeding those virus-resistant sugar canes.

5

DISEASE FROM FUNGUS PARASITES

As is well known, fungi are members of the plant kingdom. They do not have chlorophyll, and are low in the scale of evolution— somewhere close to the algae. However, there is no doubt that the largest number of plant diseases are due to fungal parasites. These organisms are so common, so numerous, and so variable in their pathogenicities that there is no wild or cultivated plant species, variety, or strain that is not susceptible to infection by some parasitic fungus. Among the fungi, the parasites look exactly like many of the non-parasitic kinds, but are far different in that they establish themselves on higher plants and utilize these hosts for nutrition and existence.

The total number of described fungus species, which include the mushrooms, comes to over a hundred thousand, including both the saprophytes, which live on manure, wood, straw, dead leaves, and other such debris, and the parasites, which cause diseases. Well over half of the fungi described in scientific writings to date are parasites, but there are probably a great many more fungi—perhaps two hundred and fifty thousand—still unknown to science. Vast tropical areas, for example, rich in microorganisms, have not been well searched for plant parasitic fungi.

There are many more fungus-caused plant diseases than is

indicated by the number of species of parasitic fungi. Many times, one fungus is to blame for several different diseases, as in *Fusarium moniliforme,* which causes a corn ear infection, a stalk rot of corn, the pokkah boeng disease of sugar cane, seedling diseases of sorghum, wilts and leaf infections of tropical range grasses, and so on. The mushroom root rot disease of fruit trees, caused by *Armillaria mellea,* affects numerous Temperate Zone bush and tree species and is also found in numerous plantation trees in Africa. One genus of crop plants with many close allies may all be susceptible to a certain fungus, like the clubroot from *Plasmodiophora brassicae* on cabbage and most of its many relatives, such as Brussels sprouts, cauliflower, and turnips. A downy mildew, *Pseudoperonospora cubensis,* diseases cucumber and related wild and cultivated crop plants. *Alternaria tenuis* attacks aging leaves of a long list of hosts, and *Botrytis* species infect fruits and faded flowers on many plants. Some crops, although they may be affected by many fungi, have one fungus for which they have a unique affinity. A rust, a certain *Hemileia,* is found solely on orchids. Other rusts are highly specialized diseases, and the same is true of some white powdery mildews. Some of the tropical black mildews are also thus specialized, but some species of *Meliola* will infect about a thousand hosts. It is conservative to estimate that, given a thousand crops, it would be easy to estimate thirty to seventy-five thousand fungus diseases.

GROWTH, FRUITING, AND SPORES

There is no such thing as a typical fungus, but a diagrammatic sketch of a theoretical fungus parasite with some of its parts is given in FIGURE 12. In this figure can be seen a mature portion represented as the mycelium or threads (also called hyphae) inside host tissues. This mycelium absorbs nutrients from the infected plant tissues. The fungus cells are attached one to another with the youngest cells at the growing tip. They may grow inside tissues or over the surfaces of a plant, sinking in occasional absorbing projections for nutrition. When a parasitic fungus fruits, it frequently pushes growth from inside the disease part to form spores outside, in the open air. Of course, if the disease is an

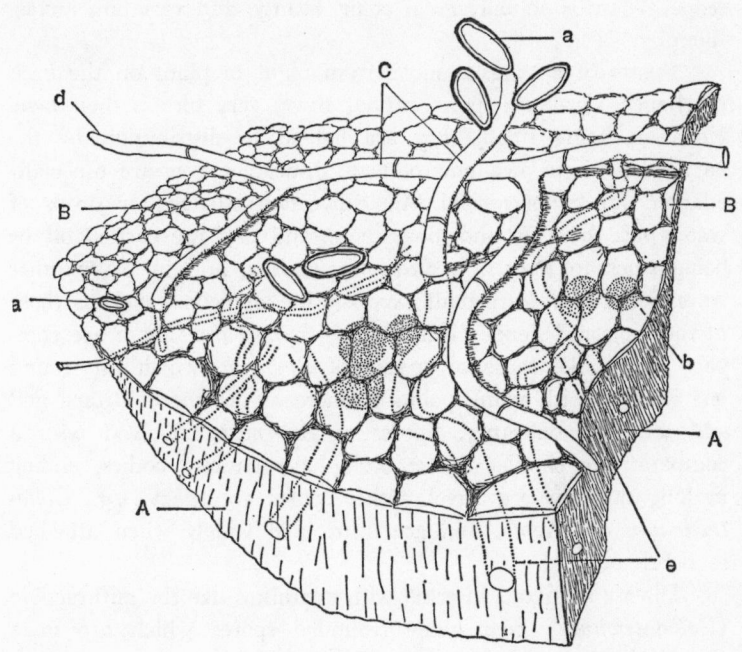

FIGURE 12 Diagram illustration of a generalized type of parasitic fungus.
A. Host leaf in cross section. B. Epidermal cells. Fungus parts: (a)
spores borne in the air; (b) spores developed inside host tissue; (c)
aerial growth of fungus; (d) growing tip; (e) mycelium ramifying inside
host.

underground infection, as is clubroot of cabbage or bean root rot,
spores are formed below ground. Spores from such infections are
loosened when roots decay, and are thus released into the soil.

   Spores are special organs of the fungus. A spore is a re-
productive structure, often simply a bit pinched off from the
fungus mycelium, produced without nuclear fusion, arising asex-
ually. It is commonly made up of a thickened wall filled with
protoplasm, awaiting encounter with its host along with the proper
conditions under which it will be able to germinate and infect.
To be fully appreciated, spores must be examined under a micro-

scope. There is actually great color, beauty, and variation among them.

Spores of a parasite move from plant to plant on the basis of chance. Ordinary spores cannot travel very far on their own. However, being small, they are helped in distribution by the vagaries of their own environment. Indeed, spores are especially adapted for being moved. Air convection currents or drops of water pick them up and move them, and they are carried off by being stuck to insects, to farm implements, and in many other ways. Some spores are built expressly for air travel, such as those of the long and slender leaf-spotting *Cercospora*. There are compact spores like those of species of *Puccinia*, which are round but studded with many points to increase the spore surface and add to spore buoyancy. Spores of *Alternaria* involved with a comparatively simple disease cycle have chubby bodies, ending in long tails for air travel. Other spores are sticky, e.g., *Colletotrichum* or *Phoma*, and are distributed widely when attached to debris or seed.

Disease on plants infected with organisms like the anthracnose (*Colletotrichum*) bear glue-surrounded spores which are in a matrix that dissolves in water, leaving them to be washed or splashed to other plants. When a drop of water with a spore in it hits a leaf and dries, the spore adheres to the leaf epidermis. When workmen brush diseased plants, they dislodge spores that are hanging in drops or are on wet surfaces; these are carried off to be smeared onto other plants. Man is one of the most effective agents for spreading spores of disease fungi from sick to healthy crops.

There are spores especially adapted to life in water, such as the ciliated zoospores of the potato blight fungus, *Phytophthora infestans*, and the *Physoderma* brown spot of corn. In such fungus species the spore bodies are scarcely more than bits of naked protoplasm. They are denser than the white of an egg, and have a pliant wall and long cilia or whipping tails by means of which the delicate organisms move in drops of dew, hydathode exudate, rain, or soil water. By far the majority of fungus spores, however, are sufficiently protected by resistant walls and cell constituents so they can live in the punishing rays of the sun, in dry air, in winter cold, and in the presence of juices from rot.

There are certain parasites that produce spores as the result of a special sexual fusion stage between nuclei, making what is called the perfect stage. These spores may be quite different from the imperfect or vegetative spores developed by the simpler asexual method. Many times the spores of the imperfect stage are merely washed off or blown away. However, there are fungi that, in connection with the perfect stage, have special mechanisms for releasing these perfect spores into the air.

There is a difference in pathogenicity between perfect and imperfect types of spores. The imperfect or asexual spore is sometimes called a conidium and is genetically identical to the mycelium from which it was pinched off. Disease caused by this asexual spore will be exactly the same as that caused by the fungus from which it originated. There is a different possibility when there has been a sexual fusion of nuclei and perfect stage spores are formed, for there is a mixing and reassortment of pathogenic and other genetic characters. It is always possible that some spores which result from nuclear fusions are mutated and are capable of causing disease in crop types and varieties never troubled before, and this is a most important consideration.

FUNGUS DISEASES

In the many thousands of plant diseases caused by fungi, there are wide ranges in degrees of severity. Some are acute and quick-acting, others are medium to chronic, and there are types in which the infections are present but have little effect—in some cases being practically benign.

The most spectacular of the fungus diseases, in either herbaceous plants or trees, are those in which there is fast kill. Sometimes there are huge, rapidly expanding leaf spots destroying much foliage. In a field or plantation, there may be a sudden and appalling collapse of a plant from root attack. This may be caused by such root fungi as *Fusarium, Rosellinia,* or *Verticillium.* Many kinds of other fungi, such as *Pellicularia,* can cause gross and rapid foliage collapse and there are thousands of plant wilts or leaf collapses. Often fungus disease becomes more severe when complicated by the presence of microscopic nematodes. These are recognized as very important organisms, although they will be mentioned only briefly here and in a few other instances in this book.

Nematodes are small, transparent, wriggling worms that need to be magnified a great deal for anatomical study. An example is the vinegar eelworm. These worms belong to the animal kingdom; many of them attack plants and are an important cause of plant disease. Scientists have determined many complex and interesting facts about their life histories: how they breed, their periods of molting, and how some of them feed upon or invade cells of plants. Diseases caused solely by the action of nematodes may result in the eating away of plant tissues, leaf spotting, and rotting of plant parts by poisons that are excreted by the parasites. In some cases there is stimulation from enzyme-like secretions. This induces abnormal enlargement of host cells, resulting in, for example, root-knot disease that is disruptive of sap flow in vascular elements and causes crop-plant wilts. Certain nematodes act as carriers of special bacterial and virus diseases, and are carried by sticky fungus spores such as those of *Colletrotrichum*. At times, numerous plant parasitic species of eelworms contaminate fields, and, when disease-causing bacteria or fungi such as *Phytophthora* are also present, the nematodes, working together with the bacterium or fungus, often cause extremely severe disease effects.

A less spectacular level of fungus disease is found which at first follows a moderate course of development and becomes very serious later. This has at times led to confusion before the course of the disease was well studied. For example, early in the growing season, appearance of a rust or a mildew may seem unimportant. As the crop matures, the disease suddenly becomes more acute. One of the fungi causing this "delayed action" is the downy mildew, *Pseudoperonospora*, on squash. Another type of which there are many is the white powdery mildew. The one on apples, caused by *Podosphaera leucotricha*, overwinters as an almost invisible infection in dormant buds. When spring comes and buds break, the fungus starts growth, and diseased buds are stunted,

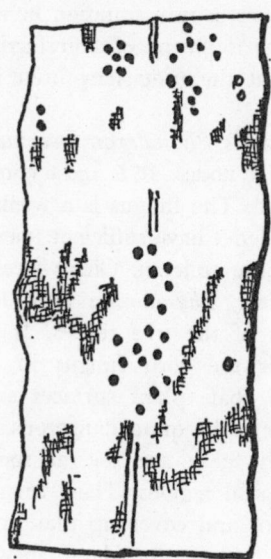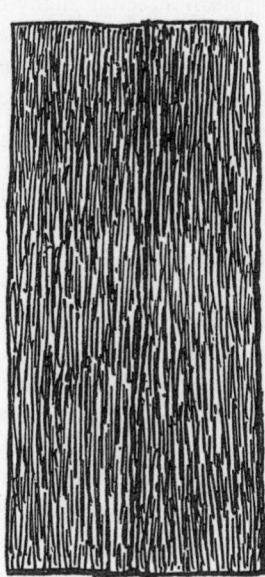

FIGURE 13 Barley powdery mildew, *Erysiphe graminis*. Right. Healthy leaf surface. Left. Mildewed, characteristic white powdery covering having millions of delicate asexual spores for wide rapid dissemination. The scattered small black bodies are perithecia containing the sexually perfect spores by which it overwinters.

stifled, and even killed. Spores from the overwintering infection go to new leaves. There the mildew attacks and appears as delicate powdery spots that spread quickly. The grain crops many times have powdery mildews, such as that on barley (FIG. 13). On whichever of the many hosts it occurs, the powdery disease is at first mild but becomes more severe as spring and summer advance.

LESS SERIOUS FUNGUS INFECTIONS

Tender roots of plants such as lettuce and cabbage frequently harbor the subterranean fungus *Olpidium*. It is a primitive type of organism affecting many hosts, but there are usually no notable disease consequences. There is, however, a rare situation in which one species of the *Olpidium* acts as a means of transferring a virus through infection of lettuce, but the fungus by itself is no cause of disease.

Another primitive type of fungus is *Physoderma zeaemaydis,* which attacks leaf bases and cornstalk nodes. It is most common where the climate is warm and humid. The fungus is a weak one and most common well-bred corn varieties have sufficient tolerance to it so that, in the main, it is of little concern. Citrus trees are invaded by a closely related organism, *Physoderma citri,* found not only in living but in dead cells of the tree tissues. It is of even less concern in citrus than is the corn fungus in corn.

A black fungus that sometimes coats plant surfaces should be mentioned here, as it may appear to be quite dangerous. It is the common sooty mold (of which there are several species) found in warm, subtropical, and tropical regions. These fungi are black epiphytes. They grow on top of and cover up plant parts; they do not infect the plant but, if very abundant, they can smother it. Another such disease is called felt, *Helicobasidium,* and it is found on bush and tree crops such as tea, coffee, and cinnamon. These growths of both *Capnodium* and *Helicobasidium* live on insect secretions and are shiny pads, or are sheaths with a fuzzy felt-like texture, and the trees affected are on the whole no more than floors or scaffolds to hold the fungus.

FUNGI VERSUS PLANTS

As in animals, where healthy skin is an excellent barrier to disease organisms, in plants, healthy, unbroken surfaces can be good barriers to infectious diseases. On the other hand, if the parasitic fungi could not manage to enter some of the protective devices of plants, these fungi would disappear from the earth. There are many parasites (like *Plasmopara viticola, Phyllachora lespedeza,* and *Alternaria solani*) that can go readily through epidermal cell coverings. A few of the means by which fungi get into plants are only suggestive of many more and of the variations that occur in disease infection.

Filaments or hyphae of a fungus may crawl all over a plant part, and certain of the threads will attach themselves quite firmly. They may enter a root hair or an opening where a secondary root breaks out of the cortex of the main root. Other hyphae pile up and exert pressure, and excretions of softening enzymes start a weakening of the root coating. Into this weak spot the fungus then penetrates. To a certain extent this also occurs with leaf infections.

An interesting succession of events takes place when certain types of fungus disease spores splash onto a leaf surface. In the anthracnoses, species of *Colletotrichum*, the spores are sticky when wet. On drying they become even stickier and so are more firmly attached. After being stuck to a leaf, the spore wall in the presence of moisture softens and sends out a germ tube. This grows a short way and then it turns down to enter the leaf. In some fungi, the germ tube swells into a specialized thickened cell that itself becomes fixed to the plant surfaces even more tightly than the original spore was. From the specialized cell or appressorium (FIG. 14) a very sharp spike is sent in from its underside that, backed by pressure, goes straight down into the plant tissue.

There also are types of infection that are very different from

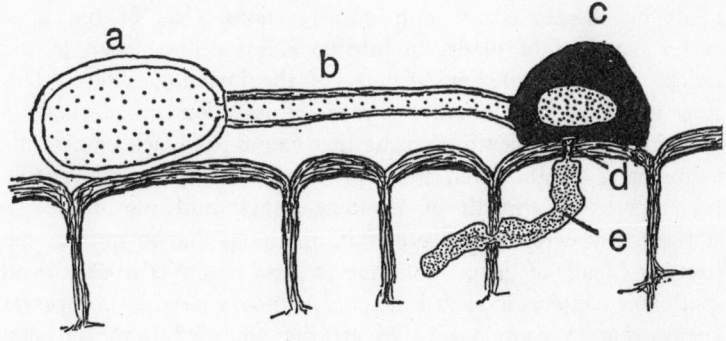

FIGURE 14   Penetration of mango fruit skin by *Colletotrichum:* (a) spore (20 microns long); (b) germ tube; (c) heavy walled, strongly adhesive appressorium; (d) needle-like peg; (e) parasite inside host cells.

this direct kind of entry. Mildew spores, as in *Phyllactinia,* may germinate on a leaf surface. But the spore sends out a germ tube that grows with great rapidity, scouting around over the leaf until it comes to one of the breathing pores or stomata, which the tube then quickly enters. From there on it is inside among the unprotected tissues. It is from the internal cells that the parasites absorb nutrients and rapidly cause leaf yellowing. Leaves then drop off so that the affected host cannot develop vigorously.

PLANTS VERSUS FUNGI—DEFENSES

Fungi and green plants have been together on earth for a long time. Green plants had to evolve means of resisting attack or they would have disappeared. The defenses they developed include such features as cell coatings, special chemical components in sap, the ability to react to enzymes or toxins, and, occasionally, certain anatomical features. It is known that natural plant openings such as leaf hydathodes are invaded by special bacteria (FIG. 5), but on the whole not by fungi. The commonly occurring natural openings on certain stems, the lenticels, mostly withstand fungi.

Fungus attacks result in many kinds of plant tissue reactions, and, the more they are studied, the more subtle some of these effects appear. Many illuminating biochemical studies have been made on disease effects and host reactions. One of the most useful reactions of plants to infections is for host tissue to die quickly in the immediate vicinity of the invading fungus. This stops plant sap from moving toward the infection and starves the parasite. It is this death of tissue that causes the black or necrotic lesion on a plant. Often these poisoned, dead parts are unable to support the growth of invading fungi, and the disease is stopped. However, there are certain organisms that in spite of the necrosis (death of tissue) continue to grow at the edge of a dead spot. This happens in such leaf spots as those caused by *Alternaria cucumerina* in cantaloupe. On growing outward from the spot center, the parasite gradually progresses farther on into the host and the spot or decay increases.

There is another type of reaction to invasion in which individual plant cells are at first stimulated. Cells at the very point of entry may be killed, but the fungus is still active. On all sides of this point, the cells divide again and again, rapidly building a sturdy swelling of small cells that keep the fungus infection well contained. Sometimes the numerous small cells around an infection will thicken their walls and deposit oils and waxes, thus forming a corky dike that holds the disease within bounds.

When infection has progressed beyond the capacity of the host to restrain its spread, the danger becomes acute. Cell walls often are pierced and sometimes roughly pushed aside by the triumphant fungus growth. In wilt diseases, internal presence of the parasite in small amount sets off violent reactions within the host. If attack is severe, there is thickening and gelatinizing of host sap so it stops water conduction in the plant vessels. This is one direct cause of wilt. In other cases, the wilt fungus grows so abundantly that it plugs the water-conducting tissues so that they cannot function. In certain conditions, the sap-carrying cells are stimulated to form nobs or tyloses that grow into the lumen of the sap-conducting part of plant vessels. Transfer of sap is thereby stopped, and the plant collapses. Discolorations result in cells that are invaded by wilt, and the cell walls are killed along with the protoplasm inside the cells. After this there is no conduction of nutrients, and the plant is sick indeed.

FUNGUS RACE DIFFERENCES AND MODERN CROPS

In some of the worst wilt diseases, the fungi involved are parasitic species of *Fusarium*. The parasites in this genus are from the soil and are well adapted to causing the diseases. Careful studies have shown that one species of *Fusarium* may have a number of different degrees of pathogenicity in the individuals or varieties within the species. Through decades of research, first by G. H. K. Link and then H. W. Wollenweber, the classification of these wilt organisms was based on morphology, using shapes and sizes of spores and character of growth in pure cultures on special media. The work was done mostly in Germany and helped pathologists all over the world. At one time, over eleven hundred species of *Fusarium* were described in literature, and an unknown culture had to be sent for identification to one of four taxonomic specialists in the genus. Species were found that were variable in almost every respect. Within a few months so many varieties could be obtained from what started as one culture that it was a major task to keep the strains separate and growing. The worst of it was that changed characters of variants of one species came within the limits of published descriptions of other variants of other species.

It was into this complexity that the team of W. C. Snyder and H. N. Hansen entered. They settled the fact that the extreme variability of *Fusarium* species was due to the rapidity with which some of these fungi mutated. Much of this needed re-evaluation, and the *Fusarium* genus was finally proved to be a highly variable group of organisms. Basing determinations on both fungus appearance and pathogenicity reactions, many groups of old species can be combined into one. There are now about ten or twelve species in this highly involved population of physiologically different races of parasites. This kind of variability is found to be of relatively common occurrence. The concept of physiologic races is always kept in mind in the work of breeding crops resistant to the variable organisms that cause disease.

INCREASINGLY NUMEROUS PLANT DISEASES

Continuous natural change is going on in the fungus parasites, causing increasingly numerous crop-plant diseases. In spite of this, and to fit the needs of farmers, modernization of crops is in progress. In old crude plantings the growers produced fair yields at the cost of painful hand labor. Fields were small, crops were moved from place to place, cultivated according to tradition, and in some (but not all) years escaped disease losses because of the haphazard way in which they were planted. Nowadays the art and science of agriculture are advancing and great stretches of land are used continuously for the same crop. They have become technologically run food factories. Machines are employed to seed, weed, fertilize, and spray various insecticides, nutrients, hormones, and fungicides, and the crop is harvested mechanically. Special crop types are bred and selected for modern production. Under these forced conditions unheard-of diseases appear and new kinds of old diseases start where old ones had at one time been stopped. As agriculture modernizes and becomes both more efficient and more professional, the plant pathologist has a greater responsibility than ever to be perpetually on the defensive.

Any important crop in the world has many diseases; sugar cane has nearly 450, coffee close to 400, citrus about 300, beans about 300, corn at least 150, and rice probably near 200. Such numbers of diseases now or soon will affect many other world crops. These crops are moved great distances from country to country, across seas and mountains to many different localities. The more they are shifted about, the greater are the chances of infections from new diseases; the new parasites come from those naturally occurring on adjacent crops or from wild growths. Unconsciously, but at the same time almost compulsively, man picks up new diseases on old crops grown for the first time in foreign lands, and brings the new infections back with him to establish them on the old crops in the old places where they were first grown.

In many cases, old crops under modern culture develop as if they were entirely different species—which is virtually what they are. With all kinds of changes, plant-disease problems change. At times, a severe disease is not altogether a bad thing when it becomes established on a crop, because one of the surest ways to guarantee the quickest, most intensive help for a crop, and therefore its betterment, is for it to be attacked by a severe disease which will then require scientists to give it greater attention than ever before.

6

FLOWERING PLANTS
WHICH ATTACK OTHERS

When one speaks of parasites, one may only think of microscopic bacteria and fungi but, of course, this is not always the case. Human beings themselves can be parasites, and men are parasitized not only by microbes but by insects such as ticks or lice, and by such large internal organisms as tapeworms. It is not so often understood that there are large flowering plants which attack crops, ornamentals, and forest growths, causing damage just as surely as the microscopic organisms.

Parasitical flowering plants come from various botanical families. Some of these, such as witchweed, attack only the roots of their hosts; some, such as most mistletoes, only the stems. Some, like dodders, flourish best on tender weeds and annual crops, and there are species of *Rafflesia* that are mostly confined to roots of jungle vines or trunks of tough trees. There is also in Australia a true conifer that is a parasite on other trees and in Brazil a broad-leaved tree that attacks other trees. In this chapter, because space is limited, we will look primarily at two major examples of disease-causing bushes and vines.

The most commonly known higher seed plants that parasitize

other plants are mistletoe bushes. There are many genera and
species of mistletoe, and the study of the botanical family
(Loranthaceae) to which they belong shows that these parasites
range from small twig-like plants to large bushes growing high
off the ground on branches of trees. They parasitize tree branches
developing holdfasts or attachments and absorbing connections,
the haustoria, by which they suck out tree juices for their own
growth. There are some exceedingly rare species that have escaped
parasitic dependence and develop as small ground-dwelling trees.
There are parasitic mistletoes distributed widely in many parts of
the world where they are serious diseases in forests, orchards, and
tree plantations. The other best-known plant-parasitic seed plant
is the dodder. Dodders are thread-like vines that twist over and
loop between their host plants, wrapping them together, holding
on, sucking out the sap, and smothering the leaves. These vines
belong to two genera, *Cuscuta* and *Cassytha*.

Dodders and mistletoes are so unusual in their habits that
they have long appealed to man's imagination and curiosity.
Theophrastus (370–285 B.C.) wrote in his book *Enquiry into
Plants* about the fact that dodders grew on other plants and how
mistletoes parasitized branches of trees.

Among the early Greeks, as Sir James Frazer shows in his
analysis of magic and religion, the mistletoe, *Viscum*, which grew
but never touched ground, was the fabled golden bough. It was
believed to bring good luck, and a branch on a door post guarded
lovers within. The juices were believed to cure diseases, could
make the sightless see, and render barren women fruitful. Dried
leaves carried as an amulet in duel or battle imparted daring,
strength, and bravery, and Druids held that an arrow of mistletoe
wood could pierce the otherwise invulnerable hearts of devils and
witches.

THE SPREAD OF MISTLETOE

Mistletoes include several genera of plants which can be distributed from tree to tree. But their seeds are heavy and are encased
in juicy fruits that, if undisturbed, when ripe and loosened will
drop to the ground where they die. Distribution is often said to

be from seeds stuck to feet and bills of visiting birds. Careful research and observation on the spread of mistletoes were made by W. Docters Van Leeuwen in the East Indies. Half a world away, in Central America, these findings were independently corroborated by my studies on the problem in plantation trees.

Mistletoe fruits are attractive as bird food. In the sweetish berries are seeds surrounded with viscid and sticky material. Birds eat the fruits, and the effect is like a cathartic. The seeds are then deposited undigested on tree stems and branches. The stringy matrix voided with the seeds is so adhesive and fast-drying that it serves to hold the seeds to the branches. Here the seeds germinate, and in the process they orient themselves with root pointed to the branch. The seedling sends out a small peg-like projection, and growths that absorb tree juices develop, thrusting down into the sapwood (sketches are shown in Fig. 15). From this time on, the mistletoe uses sap and acts as a weight, both of which injure the host.

An exception to the bird and parasite relationship is seen in certain dwarf mistletoes, species of *Arceuthobium,* which cause serious diseases in pines. When their fruits mature, the enclosed mistletoe seeds are automatically ejected into the air by strong hydrostatic force. They may be shot for forty to a hundred or more feet, depending on such circumstances as the distance of the fruit from the ground and the rapidity and direction of the wind. The sticky seeds lodge on the bark of new trees, and soon many more of these mistletoe plants are vigorously growing. In certain pine forests of the United States and Mexico, these seed-shooting mistletoes cause the most damage of any tree diseases.

THE PARASITIC LIFE

Flowering plants that are parasitic have acquired unique habits in order to prosper. All green plants have to make their carbohydrates through photosynthesis. However, in a few mistletoes, parasitism is so specialized that need for photosynthesis is much reduced. In certain dodders there are only minute scales for leaves, and vines themselves may be practically devoid of green. Certain of these parasites do not make any carbohydrates, and others have

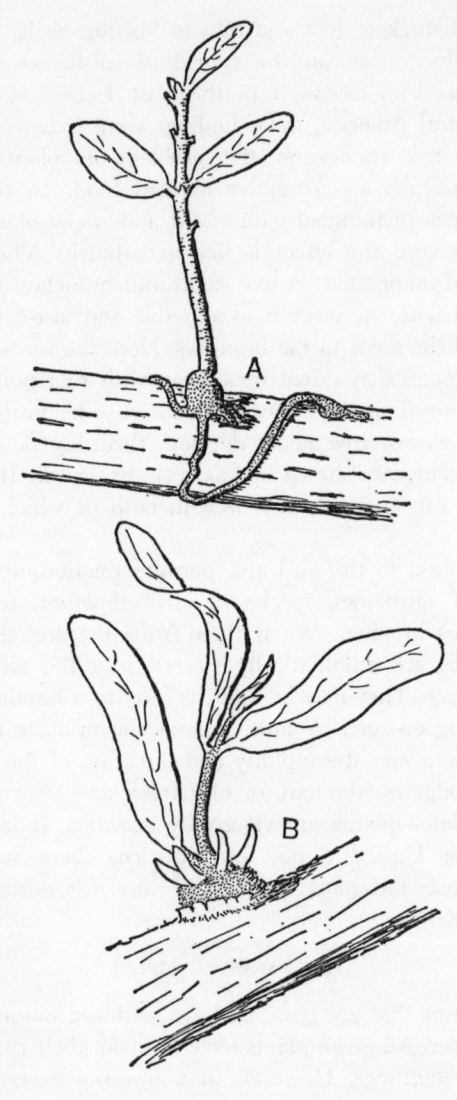

FIGURE 15 Small seedlings of different mistletoes. A. *Struthanthus*. B. *Psittacanthus*.

lost much of their photosynthetic capacity. Since these highly evolved flowering plant parasites never touch ground, they no longer absorb soil nutrients. They develop sinkers or haustoria and extract all required water and foods from their hosts. Some people say they have "evolved," some say they have "degenerated," but in any case they are adjusted to that precarious half-life of living on others.

One feature of this half-life is the use of a secondhand supply of water. On the whole, parasitic plants are not as lush in growth as are their hosts. But if a leafy branch on which mistletoe or dodder is growing is cut off, many times the first notable wilting will be that of host leaves; later the parasite wilts. The leaves of many mistletoes are somewhat leathery, and there is not as much evaporation from them as from the host leaves. With dodders, when a diseased plant is cut, the shining, smooth, and slender parasite vine remains turgid longer than the leaves of the plant on which it preys.

SPECIAL DISEASE FROM PARASITIC SHRUBS

Attacks by parasitizing shrubs or vines weaken the host plants and also cause other disease effects. Many mistletoes not only absorb sap from trees, but induce the proliferation of shoots, stunting, chlorosis, cancerous growths, branch death, and leaf deterioration. The plant parasites also open tree wood to secondary fungus decays. Mistletoes often weaken and kill what were good stands of strong, healthy trees in forests, plantations, and orchards.

On the other hand, some parasitizing plants are known to cause unhealthy stimulation of growth in the host. This has been seen in such trees as the immortelle in the West Indies, and in an inga used to shade coffee trees in Central America. Sometimes where the parasite infects, both the tree branch and the mistletoe grow at the same rate. The parasite then makes a good connection that fuses well with the host stem or branch. More commonly there is swelling and bark roughening.

In some instances mistletoes cause an increase in host metabolism. For example, a tree that is attacked may for a time produce new leaves faster than those of healthy trees. For a few months we watched a tree of a tropical croton that had lost its own leaves but was covered with the green foliage of one of the parasite mistletoes called bird vine, a species of *Phthirusa*. The host tree furnished water and nutrients from the soil for its own trunk and bare branches and the parasite carried on in its leaves the photosynthetic processes for both croton and *Phthirusa*. When the mistletoe was stripped away, the tree died.

HYPERPARASITISM AND SUPER-HYPERPARASITISM

There is a unique and interesting feature in the study of the occurrence and growth of the flowering parasitic plants. Nowhere in all biological science has man found such long series of parasites living one on top of another in complicated growth mixtures. (A diagram of one actually observed complex of this kind that I studied in El Salvador is seen in FIG. 16.) These almost indiscriminate tangles of mixed different parasitic species are found especially in tropical regions of the West Indies, Central and South America, Africa, Southeast Asia, and the Pacific Islands. In all cases they start on a host tree diseased from primary infection by a parasitic mistletoe. On this first parasite is a second parasitic species, or hyperparasite, and this in turn is sometimes diseased by a third kind, the super-hyperparasite. On top of this, a dodder vine may climb over to infect all the mistletoes. But never vice versa, for the dodders are too flimsy and slender for successful infection by a mistletoe.

In some cases, instead of a dodder, a mistletoe may surmount all as a fourth infection in a series. In rare instances there will be a fifth and even sixth, all in a tangled mass. As might be expected, there are upon them several different kinds of fungus pests, diseasing stems, flowers, and leaves of the mistletoes. Fungus parasites are found in turn parasitized by other fungi or fungus hyperparasites, fungus super-hyperparasites can in turn infect the hyperparasites. In a few cases, other fungi are found growing over the super-hyperparasites. Bacteria and viruses further increase the number of parasites on parasites on parasites, infecting mistletoes that themselves are diseasing other mistletoes on top of a tree.

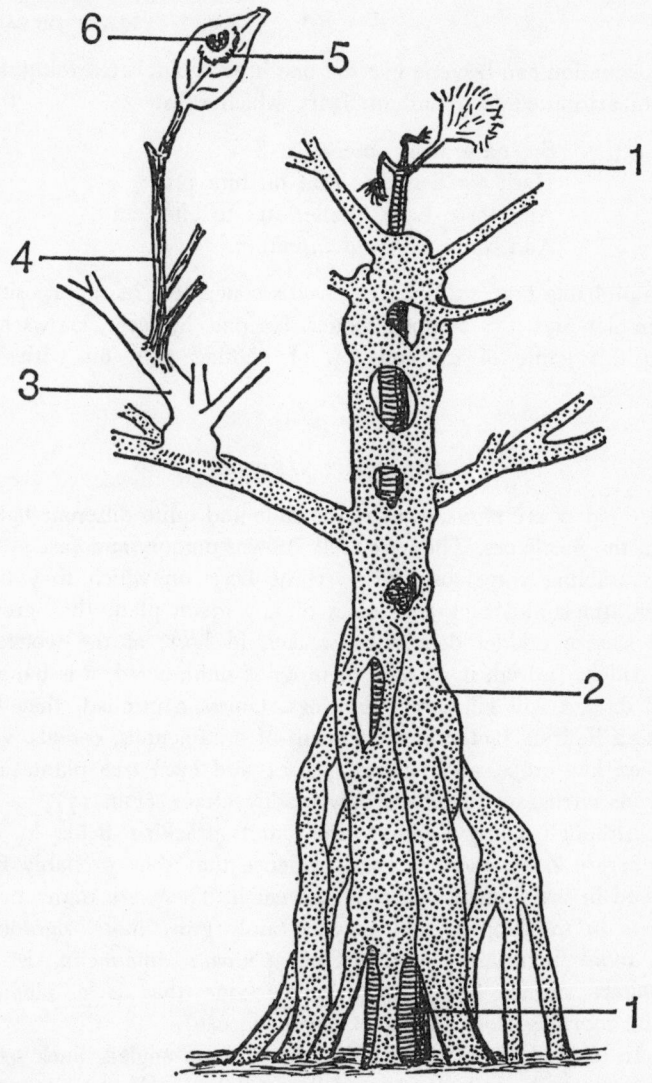

FIGURE 16 Diagram of an observed series of tree parasites, one on top of another as follows: 1. Fan palm, *Inodes* sp. 2. Strangling fig, *Ficus* sp. 3. First mistletoe, *Psittacanthus calyculatus.* 4. Second mistletoe, *Phoradendron robustissimum.* 5. Leaf spot caused by the fungus, *Uleomyces wellmanii.* 6. Another fungus attacking the leaf spot fungus, *Rosenscheldiella phoradendri.*

The situation can become like the one in that old, often misquoted poem attributed to Jonathan Swift, which runs:

> So, naturalists observe, a flea
> Hath smaller fleas that on him prey;
> And these have smaller still to bite 'em;
> And so proceed *ad infinitum*.

It is probable that, so far as the flea is concerned, its superposition is simpler and it is stopped sooner. No one, however, knows how long this game of one on top of another goes on with the mistletoes.

THE PLANT VAMPIRES

The dodders are parasites of remarkable and quite different habits from the mistletoes. They are well known, unique, and fast growing, rambling voraciously all over the hosts on which they live. They attack and suck the juices of any green plant that grows. The least a dodder does is to weaken its host; at the worst, it will kill it. Indeed, if allowed to progress unhindered, this baneful field disease will kill large plantings. Unless controlled, they become a limiting factor in the growth of ornamentals, cereals, vegetables, hay crops, and pasture grasses, and even tree plantations such as citrus, all of which they readily attack (FIG. 17).

Although many dodders are found attacking fields in the Temperate Zone, there is good evidence that they probably first evolved in warm, moist parts of the earth. There are many more species in the tropics, and they certainly grow more vigorously and more luxuriantly there. One, *Cuscuta americana*, is an especially strong, fast-growing yellow vine that is a member of the morning-glory family (Convolvulaceae).

In all dodders of this family, small, sharp-angled black seeds germinate and send down a delicate short-lived root into the soil. At the same time, a fast-growing, twisting, swinging vine end comes up that searches out green stems to attack. Once a dodder's infecting organs sink into a host plant, the parasite's root quickly withers and the vine never touches ground again. From that time on it is sucking sap and living on its green host.

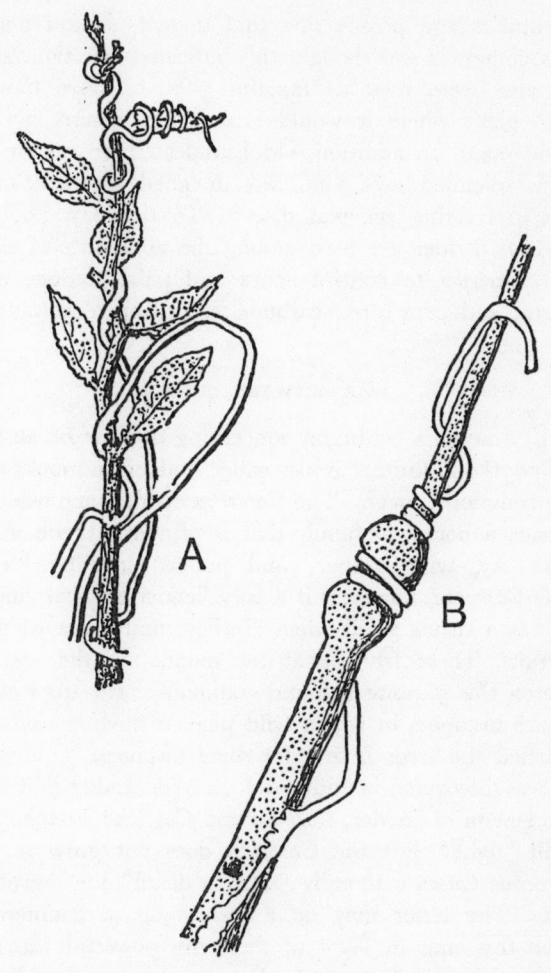

FIGURE 17 Characteristic effects from dodder, *Cuscuta americana*, attacking orange, *Citrus sinensis*. A. Enwrapping and killing a branch tip. B. Resultant swellings in small branch.

Centuries ago people saw that dodders bound and twisted plants together. It was thought this indicated affection, and pieces of the vine were used as fanciful gifts, or were moved from plant to plant where it would foretell and insure love between man and maid. In addition, old European herb doctors believed that this so-called love vine was designed as medicine by the Creator in treating venereal disease. To this day, poultices and juices from dodder are used among the aborigines of South and Central America to control aches and pains, reduce trouble at childbirth, and cure sores, carbuncles, and open wounds.

WAR BETWEEN DODDERS

There is sometimes confusion concerning dodders because another vine (*Cassytha filiformis*) is also called dodder and looks startlingly like the common *Cuscuta*. The *Cassytha* dodder vine belongs to the Lauraceae, a botanical family that is primarily made up of trees like the bay, with leathery and pungent-smelling leaves. The parasitic *Cassytha*, however, is a very slender tropical vine without leaves, has a strong smell when crushed, and bears white, round, juicy fruits. These fruits float for months in the sea, and for this reason this parasite is found commonly near tropical beaches. There are instances in which wild pigeons have fed on the fruits and carried the seeds inland for some distance.

It was discovered in India and the West Indies that sometimes the two genera of dodder, *Cuscuta* and *Cassytha*, attack each other and will "fight." But the *Cassytha* does not grow so fast and the vigorous *Cuscuta* literally "saps to death" the slower growing *Cassytha*. The latter may do a feeble job of counterattacking, but soon this ends in favor of the more powerful *Cuscuta*, with the result that the *Cuscuta* is the one that survives in an area where both may once have been.

BEAUTIFUL PARASITES

There are unusual adaptations in a higher plant if it is to carry on parasitic life. Parasitic roots become haustoria, foliage needs less water, and special means of seed distribution are developed.

But this does not mean that parasites are ugly. The growing, strangling strands of *Cuscuta* are a shining gold color; these same strands are a striking olive green in *Cassytha*. The flowers of the root-attacking *Striga asiatica* display an interesting similarity to snapdragons. Some of the mistletoe flowers, such as *Psittacanthus calyculatus*, are brilliantly red and appear like honeysuckle; in *Gaiadendron* the flowers are bright yellow and very fragrant. The largest flower that grows anywhere in the world is over three feet across and is from the parasite *Rafflesia arnoldi*, which lives on the roots of a large jungle liana in the Oriental tropics. On the other hand, very closely related to the plant with this gigantic blossom is the leafless *Apodanthes caseariae*, which has what are practically the most minute flowers extant, the size of small pinheads, pushed out from the bark of trunks and branches of certain forest trees in Central America.

7

DISEASE WITHOUT PARASITES

ᢋᢇ

During the time that the profession of plant pathology was getting on its feet in the United States, diseases from parasitic organisms commanded almost all the attention. They were very interesting and dramatic. However, plant pathologists had never entirely disregarded injuries from heat, frost, lightning, or from physiologically caused plant diseases. At first it seemed that purely physiological troubles might not be of critical importance, but certain strange effects began to be noticed. They were rather widespread, the symptoms were unusual, and no causal micro-organisms could be found. If, in one section of a country or in some particular field, the bizarre non-parasitic malady occurred, it usually took care of itself. Growers' efforts to cure it included liming, mulching, better drainage, or changing to another crop. If a different crop failed, they allowed the old land to return to trees or pasture.

But abandonment could not continue forever. Farmers and pathologists enlisted the help of soil specialists and plant physiologists. All those working on the non-parasitic maladies realized that the word *disease* did not have to mean that there was always a parasite involved. Disease is not the exact opposite of health, for there are several ways of looking at the health of a plant. For example, the housewife asks for a healthy stalk of celery—crisp, without rots or spots, at its peak of perfection. Yet her ideal celery plant has been crowded during growth, bleached, and the stalks are abnormally thickened and tender. Or take clean dry beans, shining and bright, and weighing what they should per bag. These are considered healthy even if stored so long they are dead and will no longer germinate if sown.

What about a plant on a dry and wind-swept hill that has been seared by the sun, scoured with sand, starved, and turned gray-green? Its cells are under continuous stress, but, as there are no infections by virus, bacterium, nematode, or fungus, plant pathologists may call it healthy, even if it is starved and dry. On the other hand, if the same kind of a plant grown in a moist, sheltered valley in rich soil developed little leaf symptoms from a lack of zinc, the pathologists would recognize it as having a physiological disease.

HUNGER SIGNS IN CROPS

There is no doubt that plants show symptoms of disturbance because of lack of certain chemical elements in the soil. Often the symptoms are so distinct that the cause is readily identified, as when unusual leaf patterns are seen that can be used for diagnosis. Much of the work done on such physiological disease was carried on in Florida from about 1915 to 1955. There are many other places that have these troubles, but in Florida nature furnishes good climate and there is good market for agricultural products. There is no soil in the usual understanding of the word, crops are grown in extensive fields, some of which are almost pure sand and some almost pure vegetable muck. They act like inert media; this is virtually soilless agriculture.

In Florida it was found that plants can show symptoms from a lack of general nutrition or lack of minor chemicals. Such symptoms are called hunger signs. In many instances they have special names: There is "sand drown" of tobacco, which is a magnesium deficiency; "crack stem" of celery, which is due to lack of boron; citrus "frenching" and "little leaf," which indicate a need for zinc; "dieback and blossom-end rot" on tomato when calcium is not properly absorbed; and "chlorosis" of pineapple, which means iron is lacking. As scientists in the state of Florida know, the growers cannot fail if they supply the proper nutrients, but they have to put in *all* of them. A balanced mixture of nitrogen, phosphorous, and potassium is inadequate without trace amounts of certain other elements. There is no crop of the many grown in Florida that pathologists and other agricultural workers do not study assiduously to determine the requirements for traces of needed elements.

There is a theory that during the evolution of a plant species, the elements it most frequently encounters in the soils where it grows are those likely to be most used and the least injurious to it. The most common nutrient materials are non-toxic, and these are in the usual earth compounds such as lime (mostly calcium), ocher (largely iron), sand (silicon), clay (different forms of aluminum), small amounts of sodium (salt), ash-like plant residues (much of it potassium and phosphorous compounds), and decaying protein and similar dead plant compounds (nitrogen sources). These do no harm, they are essential for plant nutrition, and they are found in most of the places that plants are.

There are many chemicals in soils in such minute quantities they are recognized only by using refined techniques. If they occur in small quantities, they are absorbed by plants. These elements— iron, sulphur, magnesium, arsenic, silver, manganese, lead, and copper—will be absorbed in excess if they are present in overlarge quantities and in an absorbable chemical form. When this happens, they may cause burn, ragged leaf effects, and other toxic symptoms. To growers, it is logical that plants are considered diseased in the strict sense of the word when they encounter either toxicity from excess or starvation from lack of an element.

INJURY FROM POLLUTED AIR

There are injurious chemicals in the air. The best-known form of air pollution is the "pea-soup" London fog, the result of millions of smoking chimney pots leading up from coal-burning stoves and fireplaces. This kind of fog is by no means restricted to London.

At its worst it kills people, and on a lesser scale reduces the quality and yield of fruits and vegetables and makes flower gardens poor and sickly.

Another kind of airborne poison is that found in the type of air pollution represented by California smog. Smog is the result of the exhausts from gasoline engines and the fumes of burned oil. Large quantities of caustic ozone develop in connection with such fumes and exhausts. If there is normal air circulation over a city it may not be bad, but when relatively stationary layers of air are interchanged, then there is danger. A warm air body, heavily charged with its poisons, is capped over by a layer or table of cold air, preventing dissipation of the ozone. This is called an inversion. Then smog is held in one place, enveloping red-eyed and sniffling human beings and settling over crops in farm lands. On plants, it causes leaf fleck and stippling, defoliation, and other major physiological diseases. Vegetables and fruits do not mature well and quality is so altered that buyers may refuse to purchase them.

DAMAGE FROM PHYSICAL CAUSES

Physiological diseases are not always connected with chemical injury; some are induced by purely physical effects. Plants use light in the process of synthesizing carbohydrates from carbon, oxygen, and hydrogen in the presence of chlorophyll. This process is called photosynthesis. One might think, then, that exposure to sunlight is always a good thing, but this is not the case. As is known by farmers, sunlight at times unduly concentrated on leaves by shining through water droplets may cause brilliant yellow ring-like injuries which can become diseased. Many crops, after having gone through long periods of wet and cloudy weather, weaken and sunburn easily. This burning is a severe disease and on fruits takes the form of scorch or scald. Growers of tender crops (e.g., citrus, tomatoes, eggplants, melons) at times may be seriously troubled with it. In scald, excess light and excess heat cause a combination of cell injuries: coagulation of the protein portion of the protoplasm, drying out of cell contents, destruction of chloroplasts, and the conversion of chlorophyll to brown substances.

Cold temperatures can also cause injury and disease. Freezing kills tissues in more sensitive plants—a fairly intricate process. At first ice forms only in the pure water that is between plant cells. The sap inside cells is a complex liquid, denser than pure water, and requires a lower temperature to freeze. When ice crystals form inside a cell, they sometimes puncture the walls. Both the sap and the cell structures are so injured that normal functions are destroyed.

Plant pathologists are sometimes called to diagnose symptoms from prolonged severe chill and from light frosts, the effects of which may be a grayish yellowing or slight necrosis of tender tip growths. Certain susceptible plants like seedling tobacco sometimes have stunted and cupped leaves. However, parts of the plant that were not frosted will continue growth. Frosts of short and less damaging duration are called white frosts. When a frost is so cold, long-lasting, and penetrating that a large proportion of cells are killed and torn, then it is appropriately referred to as a black frost. It is at the time of borderline frosts, halfway between black and white, that agriculturists can make best use of frost-fighting methods such as wind-stirring machines, spaced fires in fields, smudge pots, and water sprinkling.

Little needs to be said about the effects of drought on plants, but it is less commonly realized that plants otherwise free from disease can be ruinously affected by an excess of water just as surely as by the lack of it. Grown in a moist and tended soil, a plant takes up its needed nutrients and thrives. A sudden increase in moisture from heavy rains over a period of many days may bring catastrophe; heavy, falling drops of water that beat on the foliage along with the moisture-laden air combine to make tissues soft. If rain halts temporarily, great amounts of dew come at night and the leaf has no chance to dry. Sprays may not adhere well to such a leaf and are also diluted; indeed, some chemicals that ordinarily are good protectants become toxic in contact with long-moist foliage. With an excess of rain or irrigation, leaf cells become gorged with water and plant or tree roots standing in wet land suffer from lack of oxygen. The roots

change in color, cortex tissues are easily removed, and microorganisms are able to invade injured, weak roots that would never
have been infected under normal conditions.

EFFECTS OF PESTICIDES MAY RESEMBLE DISEASE

Plants have forever been exposed to disease arising from natural
poisons. But man has added artificially to them in modern times
to such an extent that effects from modern poisons have required
special research on the problem. This is because the hundreds
of new agricultural chemicals—fungicides, insecticides, weed kill-
ers—are being so actively used. What follows is a sampling of
kinds of plant disorders that can arise from improper use of
some of the pesticide sprays.

The most famous fungicide in the world is a combination of
copper sulphate and lime in water, and is known as Bordeaux
mixture. However, it is a spray that under certain conditions is
severely poisonous to some kinds of vegetables and trees—for
example, the cucumber or the peach. Young leaves may be
partly killed and older foliage show brittleness, browning, and
defoliation. Where symptoms of injury are disregarded, permanent
harm can come to plants if they are too heavily sprayed with this
fungicide. One component of Bordeaux is a copper compound and,
with many applications annually, as much as three to five hundred
pounds of copper can accumulate per acre of soil in a matter
of twenty-five to thirty years. Such a concentration stunts plant
growth, kills earthworms, and so disturbs the balance of the
soil flora that the land requires special treatments to neutralize
copper toxicity.

Certain organic sprays are now used in place of the copper-
containing Bordeaux. Some have been better than anything anyone
ever dreamed would develop, but, as good as Maneb, Zineb,
and Ferbam are, they can cause chlorosis, stunting, and other
distinct injuries to young seedlings of some of the more tender
crops. In consequence, the farmer who uses them has to be on
the watch—just because a certain amount is good is no reason
to apply twice as much, expecting it to be that much better.

The herbicide, 2,4-D, that kills broad-leaved weeds, is

sprayed on fields to destroy stretches of unwanted growth, and sometimes the spray drifts away from the applier. At distances of as much as a mile or more downwind, severe leaf twistings, distortions, and even plant death may occur.

There are numerous new spray compounds containing special forms of copper. Ordinarily some are used very successfully for long periods, and are fully accepted, but at times only one application of some of these proprietary sprays has been known to cause bronzing and stiffness in young coffee leaves, purple to bronze discolorations on banana foliage, and brown spots on leaves of certain Temperate Zone orchard trees.

Spraying with arsenic components can result in serious internal effects under special conditions. In some hosts, application of sprays of this sort causes symptoms that are reminiscent of certain minor element deficiencies, and, on diagnosis, when an indicated minor element is supplied to the leaves, often the abnormal symptoms are cured.

When DDT first came on the market as the wonder of wonders among insecticides, it was applied freely on plants in large quantities and proved to be an excellent insect killer. It is known now, however, that this insecticide has a toxic effect, slowing down growth when too much is used.

8

SOME ADDITIONAL AND NOTABLE DISEASES

It is impossible in a short book even to approach a complete review of the multitude of diseases affecting plants. More detailed information in texts and articles, lists and the like, may be secured through purchase or by request from authorities in state and national governments, and from libraries. To complete this book's plant-disease story, however, we should mention certain other outstanding diseases. This will by no means cover all the remaining plant diseases, but will give the reader some insight into the size and complexity of the study of plant pathology today.

DISEASE OF YOUNG PLANTS

In gardening operations, it is common practice to produce young plants from thickly sown seeds. Soon after planting, the seedlings sprout up all at once, thick, crowded, all of a size, and dark green. This occurs before any fungus present in the soil has time to attack; but now the young seedlings are extremely susceptible to damping-off disease.

Just when new seedlings appear most promising, and almost any kind are susceptible, if damping-off fungi are there, trouble starts suddenly. It shows up in small centers, quickly spreading outwards. Seedlings "drop dead" almost before the farmer's eyes.

Damping-off disease is caused by twenty-five or thirty kinds of fungi, but there are two main culprits. Both are very widespread. One of them is *Rhizoctonia solani* and the other is *Pythium debaryanum.* When conditions are favorable, they kill seedlings at and just above the soil line, but sometimes with the coming of dry weather damping-off may stop. It is not surprising that a young seedling is highly susceptible to damping-off, for during seed germination and early growth, cells are enlarging at a great rate, growing so fast that the cell walls are stretched thin. At this point the thin cell walls can be easily penetrated by attacking fungi, and damping-off may well occur. As soon as a very young seedling stem is infected, epidermal and cortical cells are killed, and in a few hours the whole plant collapses, dead on the ground.

Damping-off is not just confined to infection by fungi already in the soil. Even in sterile soil, damping-off contaminations can be planted with seed as invisible spores. If the fungus growths start soon enough the seed may be killed before it can grow, but if germination does proceed, the emerging young seedling is infected and dies from damping-off. As seedlings age, they become tougher and do not collapse quickly when attacked by a damping-off fungus. When infected, the more mature, stronger plant tissues at the soil line are more likely to develop a firm decay. This may occur from many disease organisms. Two examples of this kind of disease on older tissues, from infection by *Sclerotium* and *Rhizoctonia,* are shown in FIGURE 18. Such injury would never occur if proper field rotations or seed- or soil-disease-prevention treatments were practiced.

Formaldehyde was discovered in 1867 but was not used for damping-off control or as a seed disinfectant until 1888. By 1891, H. L. Bolley had reported successful formaldehyde treatment of seedling and seed-borne diseases of potato and grains. Formaldehyde soon became a standard for control of seedling diseases, but it could be toxic, needed to be handled with great care, and had limitations. Scientists later changed to other seed treatments

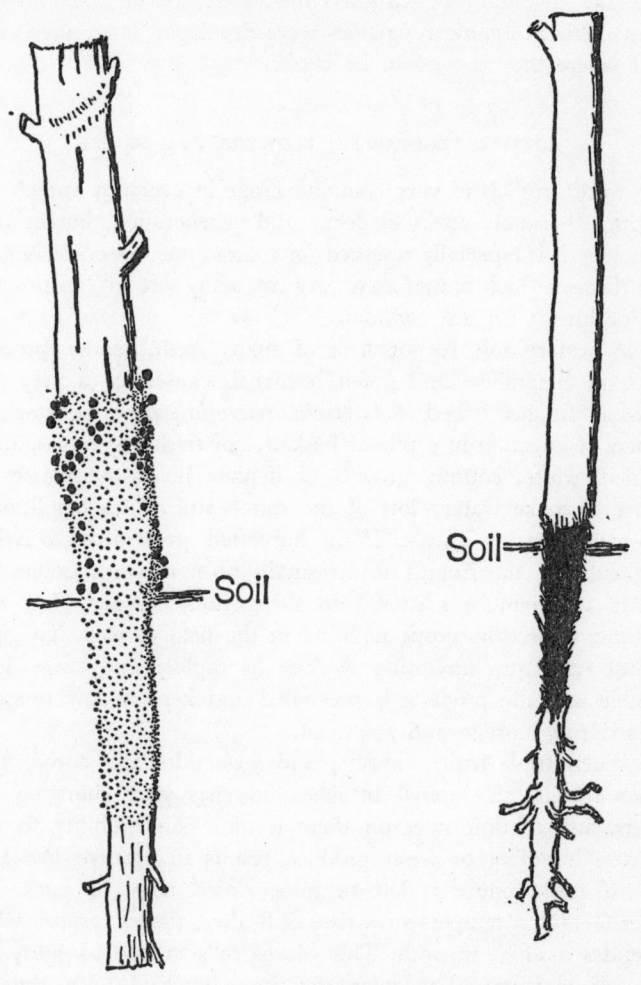

FIGURE 18 Infection soil line in old seedlings: symptom on cotton (left) of *Sclerotium rolfsii* rot; white cottony growth covers invaded area, with small, round sclerotia studding its surface. Effect on tobacco (right) from *Rhizoctonia solani* attack; diseased tissue black and sunken.

with the invention of various fungicides, stickers, and wetting agents. When organic fungicides were developed later, these were used where they proved to be better.

ROTTING VEGETABLES, FLOWERS, AND FRUITS

The word "rot" is of very common usage in everyday speech and writing. It usually refers to decay and degeneration, but in plant pathology it is especially reserved for a large number of decomposition diseases. Such names as watery rot, slimy soft rot, anthracnose rot, or brown rot are common.

A watery soft rot or leak of many fresh, tender products (such as cucumbers and green beans) is caused by a very fast-growing fungus called *Sclerotinia sclerotiorum*. This starts at centers of infection in a pile or basketful of fresh vegetables, and a tangled, white, cottony growth of hyphae holds the masses together to make watery lots of the rotted stuff. This condition is also called nesting disease. If the harvested green produce is kept long enough, the fungus forms small, resistant dark bodies like bits of rat manure scattered in the cottony strands of a nest. At times it destroys crops standing in the field as well. To guard against such rot, harvesting is done as rapidly and carefully as possible and the produce is precooled and kept at low temperatures during storage and shipment.

When fresh fruits, flowers, and vegetables are stored, their tissues soften, chlorophyll bleaches, starches start changing into sugars, and as time goes on there is more susceptibility to rots. Careless handling of fresh produce results in massive loss from rots. If the produce is left in piles, closed bags, or packed in boxes or crates, temperatures rise. Still alive, tissues respire, which generates a slight warmth. This causes cells to lose turgidity and give off moisture. The microorganisms involved with rots are always present in storage, and this hot, moist environment can be ideal for them. With a little encouragement the stage is set for disease.

The most common, best-known market disease of fresh groceries is slimy soft rot. This ubiquitous rot was given detailed attention by L. R. Jones, who published the results of his study in now-classic papers in 1901 and 1909. Not only was this rot found to affect most vegetables, but it also shortened the life of cut flowers. This rot has been known a long time; in his Sonnet 94 Shakespeare sadly noted its effect on the lily. The bacteria which cause this rot, *Erwinia carotovora*, are in soil, drainage water, stuck to debris, attached to dust particles, on floors and benches or sorting tables, smeared onto and dried inside and outside harvest equipment, gummed to hands of laborers, and on the blades of the knives and scissors used for cutting and trimming. Once the organism enters a wound and is warmed, it quickly starts decay. Diseased parts become soft as the cells disintegrate and separate from each other, and nauseous slime and sticky juices ooze out.

To reduce slimy soft rot, scrupulous attention is given to cleanliness in harvest and handling. Freshly cut plants are kept clean and cool. Work is progressing in the use of deeply penetrating gamma radiation, since it has been found that ionizing radiation will eliminate the slimy soft-rot bacteria. The radiation-treated produce will keep weeks, in some cases even months, at room temperatures.

There are a large number of species of the fungus *Glomerella* (also called *Colletotrichum*), which causes anthracnose rots. The microscopic spores germinate and penetrate fruit (Fig. 14) and vegetable surfaces, but for some time do not grow far internally. Then, when tissues ripen, the anthracnose infection suddenly shows up as a dark rot. On peaches the fungus *Monilinia* causes brown rot. Even if it has infected the fruit, at first it is not seen on newly picked firm fruits. However, as the peaches age, infections quickly become dark brown decay. It destroys the appearance, and even a small amount of rot spoils fruit flavor.

WILT COLLAPSE AND DECLINE

The *Fusarium* tomato wilt is an interesting plant disease to consider, since it has several readily recognized, well-studied characteristics. Detailed researches in greenhouse and laboratory have shown that complete kill results once the disease fungus enters a susceptible plant under optimum conditions. In the field, sick-looking plants appear, usually about the time fruits are forming.

Leaves droop and die on one side, then yellowing sets in, and
after that the whole plant wilts and dies. Distinct browning is
clearly visible in the vascular elements that carry the sap from
roots to the sick leaves, the drying stems, and the stunted fruit.

Several other very serious diseases are known as "the wilt."
There is a cabbage wilt not due to a *Fusarium*-type fungus. A special parasitic fungus, *Plasmodiophora brassicae*, is associated with
the disease, known as clubroot, which is most prevalent in cool,
acid, and moist soils. It occurs in Russia and in many parts of
continental Europe, England, North America, and in some other
countries as well. In many regions it prevents full productivity of
such cruciferous crops as cabbage, radish, table and stock turnip,
kale, rutabaga, and mustard. In its first stages, young glistening

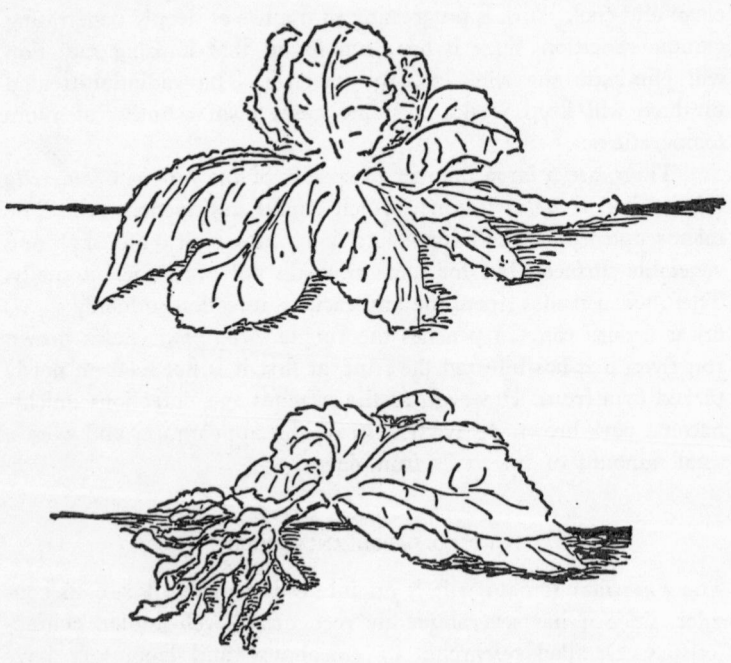

Figure 19 Cabbage plant wilted and dying from clubroot, *Plasmodiophora brassicae;* pulled to exhibit root swellings (bottom).

green leaves of cabbage that give promise of an excellent crop turn dull, suddenly sag, and develop what is known as flagging (Fig. 19). The roots are tremendously malformed and cannot properly absorb water and nutrients from the soil. Decay organisms enter the distended, swollen parts that rot off. No plant with such affected roots can be expected to develop well.

The problems in wilt collapse are intriguing and of practical as well as theoretical importance. The wilt disease symptoms are not altogether due to loss of water and subsequent drying. There are poisons involved, changes in the cells of the diseased plants, along with plugging of water-conducting tissues. Not only bacteria, nematodes, and fungi cause wilting, but also viruses, such as the rose wilt virus of Australia and New Zealand.

There is a broad range of types of wilts, diebacks, and collapses. It is a large subject, to which numerous professional plant pathologists have given their most serious thought and attention. The whole environment is involved—soils, air, water, temperature, and the many other organisms surrounding the crop plant. Field work has been essential in these studies. At first it was all done in the fields themselves, under exhausting conditions, limited by the distance a man could walk with his equipment. But now aerial photography, adapted from war techniques, has been perfected and is used for extensive field surveying. This kind of help in the air age is most useful in plant pathology. By employing proper equipment, with special filters in the cameras so plant diseases are identified on photographic prints, by proper planning of experimental areas to be photographed, and by spacing intervals between retaking of pictures, it is possible to learn more and to cover a much greater area in field work. It is now used in studying field spread of wilt in bananas, pineapple, beans, flax, coconut, tobacco, cereals, tomatoes, sugar cane, rice, and in forests and in pastures.

SPOTS AND MOLDS ON LEAVES

Spots and molds are so common on the leaves of both wild and cultivated plants that the lesions are usually accepted as normal features in nature, hardly worthy of notice. Many times leaf spots occur purely from physical injuries or physiological effects on leaves. Nevertheless, most leaf spots are from microorganisms, are diseases of great economic significance, and come from infections by parasitic microorganisms. Spots are of various colors and configurations. Some of the causal organisms are bacteria, some are viruses, and some are nematodes, but by far the largest number are fungi. There are well over fifty thousand plant parasitic fungi known to attack leaves, causing a few hundred thousand kinds of spots and other blemishes.

Though the variety in leaf spots is almost limitless, perhaps one of the most spectacular is the fast-expanding red leaf spot disease, *Sclerotium coffeicola.* It is found on large Liberica coffee leaves, and appearances may be complicated by the fact that certain of these spots change in shape and color with age. There are parasites that infect several diverse host plants, looking like one thing on one and like something very different on another. There are some unusual leaf spots caused by a species of *Mycena* that are known to be luminescent, giving forth a weird and ghostly light when seen at night (FIG. 20).

CANKERS AND FIRM ROTS

In 1637, Milton wrote, "As killing as the canker to the rose." This was a poetic reflection of an ancient knowledge about cankers, which were so common in those days he knew it would have universal meaning. Cankers on a tree are delimited, corroded, sunken, and dead sores on stem, branch, or trunk. Infections may start small, but often show evidence of enlargement that has healed. The disease may subsequently break over the healing, the new edge heal again, then disease may break out yet again. Several kinds of fungi cause cankers on woody stems: *Cytospora* on fir; *Melanconis* on birch; *Coniothyrium* on rose; and *Endothia* on chestnut. Cankers cause general weakening of the entire tree or bush.

Serious though cankers are, wood rots caused by deep infections of fungi (FIG. 21) are as dangerous to trees, and often the causal fungi are more easily recognized. These rots are of many types and make an extensive list. When cut into and tested, some

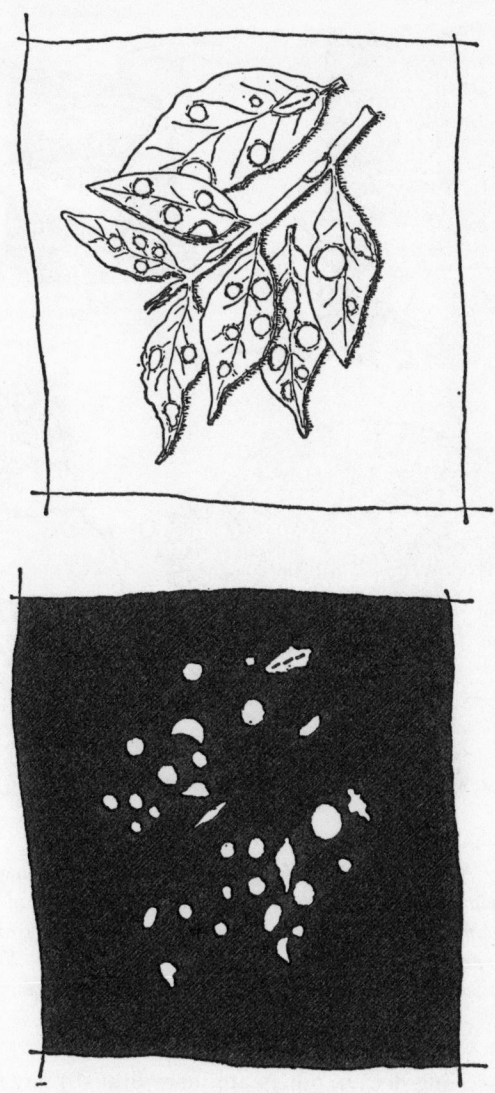

FIGURE 20 Stem and leaf spots on coffee from the American leaf spot, *Mycena citricolor*. Top. As viewed during the day. Bottom. Same spots luminescent at night.

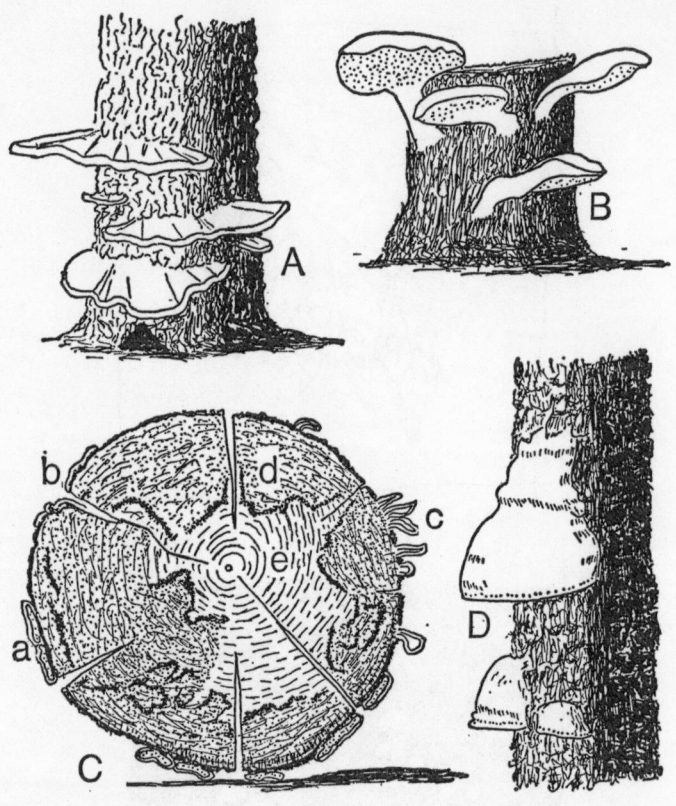

FIGURE 21 A few wood-decay fungi: A. At base of dying hackberry some *Fomes applanatus;* B. Stump of albizzia with conchs of *Ganoderma pseudoferreum;* C. Cross section of decaying oak log, showing: (a) attack of *Lenzites;* (b) *Polystictus* fruiting bodies; (c) *Stereum;* (d) fungus-invaded wood; (e) uninvaded. D. Trunk of dead pine with *Fomes pinicola.*

cause soft-feeling decays, others are more firm. In any case certain of the fungus growths from the rots are very spectacular.

There is a long tradition in art in which gnarled trees with dying branches and gaping holes in their trunks are subjects of attractive, moody, and romantic sketches and paintings. Nature lovers and bird watchers think of holes in trees as good homes for wild life. Yet these cavity homes are actually signs of special disease. The rot penetrates deeply and the bark may show a wave-furrowed, roughened condition that extends downward far below the hole.

Disease infection in either trees or bushes may take place without wounds, but a stub left from pruning is often the opening for which spores from disease-producing organisms have been waiting. On the cut surface they will germinate quickly and grow into the stub, causing decay. At first, symptoms are not readily observed, but in a few weeks, rot is more evident, the disease extends into the healthy bark and may even girdle the stem. Often as a canker ages, small colored kernels stand out on its surface arranged in rows or clumps, or in graceful concentric circles. These kernels are fungus growths, and inside them, spores develop by which the disease spreads.

CHANGE AND STAGES OF DISEASE OCCURRENCE

The progress and change of tree disease, whether in wild or managed forests, in indifferently cared-for tropical tree plantations, or in well-cutivated Temperate Zone orchards, is about as follows. The first stage is when seeds germinate and the new, tender plantlets are susceptible to damping-off (*Rhizoctonia*), which will thin out the seedlings. After survivors have grown through the juvenile condition, the time comes when mild to severe leaf and twig spotting may occur. During this time, these troubles may be aggravated by the weakening of seedlings from lack of shade, poor soil, excessive rainfall, and other natural conditions. As the small trees grow and change or are set in the field they lose their seedling character and the new bark begins to protect stems from disease, though in some cases infections gain entrance under the bark by following down leaf petioles into the whip wood and by invading through an insect-feeding injury or other wound.

Trees that are no longer seedlings become vigorous, soft saplings; this is often the time of infection by nematodes, virus, bacteria, rust, and other fungi which are not so often found at younger stages. As saplings grow into hard but not yet mature trees, leaf and twig diseases become more severe. At this time there is an increase in dieback, canker, stem or trunk rot, and root collapse. Then as trees become old, *Fusarium, Phytophthora,* and other root diseases become more common and are increasingly more noticeable.

DEFORMITIES, GALLS, AND MONSTROSITIES

A large number of plant diseases cause abnormal, dramatic growths. The display of deformities and monstrosities from increases in cell sizes or cell numbers, and combinations of both, indicates that something is definitely wrong. These common symptoms are exciting to see, and many species of plants are subject to them. One type of monstrous growth is that found on Camellia from attack by *Exobasidium camelliae* on leaves.

The crown gall, caused by a bacterial organism, *Agrobacterium tumefaciens,* is a severe root and plant base disease often mentioned as a remarkable example of tumor formation. This swelling looks like a boiling and seething mass of poorly organized, undetermined tissues, and often results in plant death. Another soil-inhabiting disease bacterium brings about an exaggerated growth in the root region, but the gross appearance is very different. This disease is known as hairy root, caused by *Agrobacterium rhizogenes.* When a healthy cutting is planted in a contaminated medium and roots start to grow, the bacteria attack the cells that are breaking forth from root initials. Instead of a normal number of robust, healthy roots, very many weak and subnormal diseased roots are produced. Roots infected by hairy root do not absorb well, they decay quickly, and the affected cutting is useless. Certain other galls, although of lesser size than some, may, as in the case of onion smut (FIG. 22), be numerous and cause severely debilitating effects.

LEGUME NODULES AND PLANT ROOT KNOTS

It is well known that nitrifying bacteria (*Rhizobium* spp.) infect roots of legume crops. In its strictest sense this might be called a disease, but it is not thought of in that way. An abundance

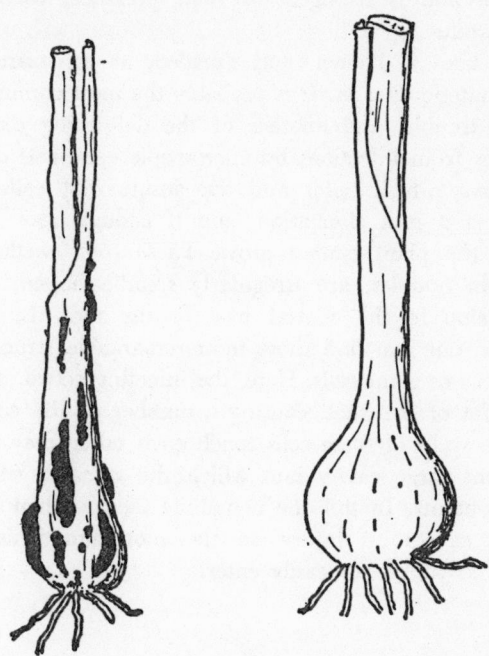

FIGURE 22 Onion smut, *Urocystis cepulae,* galls on young white onion plant compared with an uninfected onion.

of the galls it causes is actually welcomed by agriculturists. In the galls, the bacteria absorb nitrogen from the air and form protein, some of which is absorbed by the legume, while a large amount of it remains as fixed and usable nitrogen in the galls or nodules. When these become detached in the soil and decay, soluble nitrogen, as much as over two hundred pounds per acre, is left from these galls. To set these legume root galls apart from other neoplasms, specialists refer to them as root nodules. Nodules remind one of small, tightly closed, lumpy bags. They are attached along the side of a root by a little, narrow connection. This slender part is such that the nodule may be cut away or plucked off without much difficulty. A legume root which bears nodules grows well and is stronger for their presence, thanks to their nitrogen-producing ability.

Root knot is known, and dreaded, as an example of one of the nematode diseases. It is probably the most commonly known nematode trouble, and another of the deforming diseases. Root knot comes from infections by microscopic eelworms of the genus *Meloidogyne*, which enter and live inside root cells. Root-knot infections stop root elongation, and if enough roots have knots on them, the plant cannot grow. These root swellings, so different from nodules, are irregularly spindle-shaped, rough, and often develop in the central part of the root. By use of the microscope, one can find those most remarkable structures in the knots known as giant cells. Here, the infecting eelworm has settled at one point of the knot, causing a number of the cells to swell. Where the walls of these cells touch each other they disintegrate, forming one large cavity into which the diseased cells pour all of their contents. In this the nematode feeds. When a root knot decays, it causes an injury on the root into which parasitic bacteria and fungi can easily enter.

BURLS AND GALLS

Many of the deforming diseases thus far mentioned are in herbaceous crops. But monstrosities and distortions are common on trees and bushes as well. A remarkable example is the burl. Fine cabinet-wood trees are often susceptible to fungus infections by species of *Sphaeropsis*, which form gnarled swellings or burls that do not kill or even much hinder tree development for years. Cabinet workers do not think of a burl as a disease, however, since this wood is hard, takes on good finish, and is therefore useful in inlay and other work.

It is fortunate that many tree deformities are in leaves, as those are the parts most readily discarded. A famous and ancient tannin source is the Aleppo gall. This deformity is caused by a wasp-like insect that lives in gall tissue of a scrubby, tough oak in the Near East. Mites cause flattened oyster galls on oak leaves so that they may drop about midsummer, long before they should. Insect galls come on twigs and are even caused on such lowly plant types as lichens, mosses, and algae.

Some leaf galls are from fungi, but not many. Peach as well as plum leaves are twisted, swollen, and deformed in a most exaggerated way by the leaf-curl disease caused by *Taphrina*. In corn, a gall forms; ears are grossly enlarged and deformed by smut, *Ustilago maydis*, and these diseased tissues become gorged with black spore masses. In a very different manner on cranberry leaves small bright-red galls are formed by *Exobasidium vaccinii*.

9

PROBLEMS IN CONTROL OF DISEASES

No one knows how many diseases there were in prehistoric crops, but certainly there were many. As soon as man began selecting a plant, it was grown in patches. As the patches were replanted year after year, diseases appeared, prospered on the large number of similar hosts brought together in the patch, and continued to increase. Even if one could give a close estimate of the number of plant diseases today, he would shortly have to revise it upward. More diseases constantly appear on old crops, new crops that are brought from the wild have new diseases, and these quickly go over to attack old crops.

All the academic duties, reading, teaching, and research, in a plant pathologist's life have one central purpose, and that is to control plant diseases. It may seem that pathologists have been overly interested in the names of fungi, the genetics of plants, enzymes and toxins, infection problems, and the nature of the cell wall, but all of these abstruse features lead to an understanding of disease control. This is the practical side of plant pathology and those in the science are proud of it.

ANCIENT MAN'S CONTROL OF PLANT DISEASE

Even before the organized body of knowledge and way of thinking we call Science had become part of human activity, man
was doing his best to control field and garden diseases. Greeks
and Romans moved their crop-growing to areas where grain rusts
were less severe. Those with blighted vineyards and orchards
changed from disease-ridden, moist valleys to better slopes where
plants could be grown in drier, less disease-prone regions.

The pruning of trees and vines was known a long time ago
to be a sound means of reducing diseases. It was done at first
mainly to make some sense and order out of the wild tangle
foliage will develop if left on its own, but it soon became evident
that taking off overgrown branches also resulted in better fruits
and less disease. So disease reduction by husbandry methods of
this kind had actually developed before the birth of scientific
agriculture.

African women with short-handled hoes and tropical Americans with iron-tipped or stone-tipped planting sticks cleverly plant
seeds in new clearings where soils are shallow. They know that
crops are much healthier in such fields if the fragile tropical
soils are kept littered with debris; they plant both by design
and by tradition in an irregular fashion, and in mixed stands.
Then helpful outsiders arrive with their modern methods to
demonstrate clean plots, plowing, smoothing, and growing one
crop in handsome rows, and disease marches in.

The reason for this strange situation is that the tradition-
taught indigenous farmers in the world tropics, without analyzing
why, keep a balanced condition by their cropping methods, and
thereby avoid much disease. Sometimes what they do is as simple
and natural as abandonment and moving to a new place. This
kind of agriculture consists of the felling and burning of trees
in an area, growing a few years' crops in the field, and then
leaving it for a freshly felled and burned neighboring clearing.
In seven to nine years the land returns to second-growth forest
and growers can farm it again.

Some husbandry methods and systems among primitives are

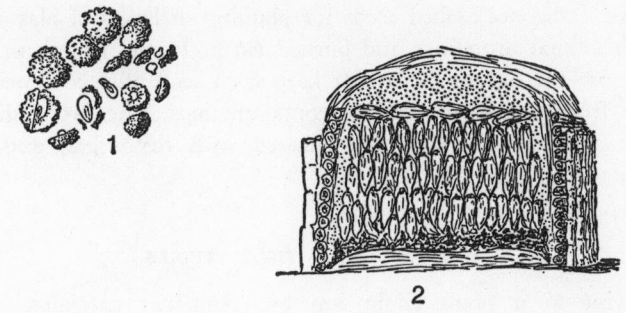

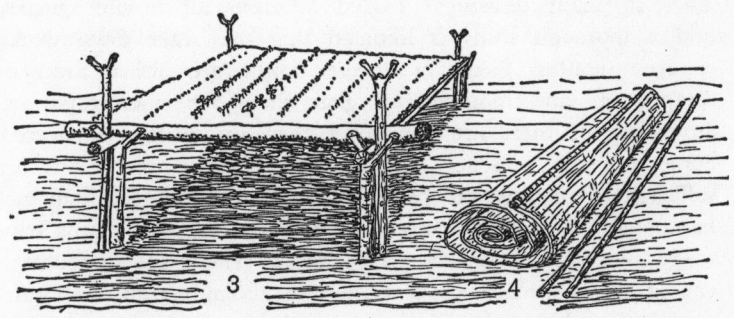

FIGURE 23 Examples of peasant methods of protecting seeds and seedlings: 1. Seeds for planting embedded in clay mixtures. 2. Half-exposed pile of carefully stacked seed corn ears in husks, surrounded by ashes and shielded from moisture (always placed under a roof). 3. In wet rain forest, seedbed on a raised platform of forest materials. 4. Matting roll of corn and reed stalks, supported above seedbed to keep off rains and long-lasting dews.

fairly sophisticated. They have learned that the lives of some of their plants are prolonged by stripping off spoiled leaves when first disease spots appear. Some Central Americans sprinkle powder from certain volcanic rocks, or road dust mixed with ashes from guarumo wood, on foliage and along rows of seedlings. They also protect seedlings (FIG. 23) on raised platforms that can be covered with mats against heavy rains and prolonged dews. Indigenes embed seeds for planting in layers of clay mixed with animal droppings and burned earth. In the Americas, some still use the old methods that keep corn seed alive and perfectly free from insects and disease contaminations. The dry, unhusked ears are stacked (FIG. 23) encased with dry ashes, and kept sheltered from the rains.

CLINICAL AND FIELD STUDIES

A visit to a plant clinic run by competent specialists is an illuminating experience; such an organization is of truly inestimable value as help to know what disease occurs and how to control it. There a plant disease is looked at from all possible angles, and a thorough study is initiated that may take days, weeks, or even months. Pieces of diseased tissue are picked away or scraped off and mounted on glass slides for microscopic examination. If there are nematodes they are quickly discovered. Sometimes the presence of spores or the fungus threads are sufficient to identify the pathogen; in other cases this may not be enough. If a virus seems to be involved, healthy plants have to be inoculated with disease material. Where the difficulty is caused by a fungus or a bacterium, isolations to laboratory media must be made. If the diseased bit of tissue contains a parasite, fungus, or bacterium, the organisms will push out of the infected material and grow on the medium. From this growth, the microorganism is transferred to other agars, and pure cultures of it are used to prove by Koch's postulates whether it is the cause of the disease. With suspected nematode disease, it may be necessary to take soil from around roots, and by special methods have the eelworms washed out of the soil and then examined microscopically.

For an adequate diagnosis, a pathologist also needs to find out how the unknown disease develops in garden or field. Is it common and serious? Do insects carry it? Is it only in certain soils? Does it occur in sheltered or open places? Does it stay from year to year in some special form? Is it carried by winds or rains? In what season of the year does it first appear? Answers to these and many other questions must be found.

ENVIRONMENT AND DISEASE

Weather makes a great difference in plant diseases as related to rain, hot days, drought and dew, winds, dust, sunlight, shade, and other factors. Diseases are known that are especially adapted to the hot steamy tropics. Some do well only in drier, colder regions of the Temperate Zone. Some disease fungi produce light-weight spores readily spread by air currents that sweep them above the clouds into slip streams that can eventually deposit them all over the planet.

Spring, with its recovery from the death of winter, is the time when rain brings spores down from the air. Dampness increases the severity of certain leaf spots, favors damping-off, and helps the infectious rot of planted seeds before they can even germinate. As summer advances, the story changes. The growth of plants progresses; leaves, roots, and stems accumulate food, flowers open, and fruit begins to set. With increased sun and warmth, diseases appear along with the new growth in the developing crops.

One of the goals of plant pathology has been to study the effects of weather under as nearly controlled conditions as possible. At one period of work on plant diseases, no single kind of research produced so rich a harvest of results as did experiments on the effects of nothing more than temperature in relation to plant disease. It was because of the leadership and shrewdness of Professor L. R. Jones that the now-famous Wisconsin Soil Temperature Tanks (FIG. 24) were perfected. They are extremely useful in understanding plant diseases, and similar "tanks" are now found in plant research centers all over the world.

In simple terms, tanks are constructed with compartments holding water maintained at different temperatures. Soil containers with inoculated plants growing in them are placed in these temperature-controlled compartments so that the water surrounds them. Incubating a disease soil which has plants growing in it results in the disease appearing at the soil temperature for which it is best suited. Grown side by side, temperature effects on diseased plants are clearly seen. A disease that occurs

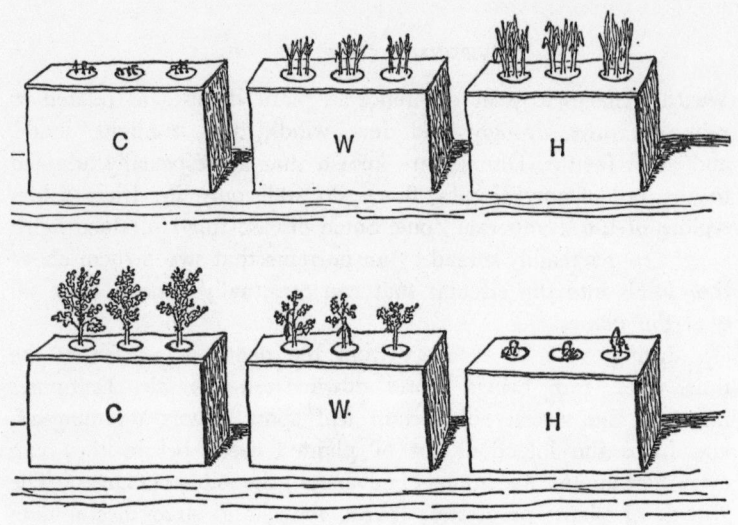

FIGURE 24 Wisconsin temperature tanks filled with water held at various temperatures duplicating effects of seasons or regions (e.g., C-cool, W-warm, H-hot); water circulating around containers of disease soil maintain root temperatures in plants grown in them: Top. Onions differently diseased by smut, *Urocystis cepulae*, which is a cool season or region disease. Bottom. Tomatoes with differing amounts of wilt effect growing in soil infested with wilt, *Fusarium oxysporum lycopersici*, which is a hot season or region disease.

solely in a cool or a warm region, or in early spring or in midsummer, is better understood when it is studied in these temperature tanks. Effects of switching temperatures back and forth can be observed, differences in diseases can be followed in wet or in dry soils and at various temperatures. Tank studies disclose temperatures at which plant disease resistance is good, and the temperatures that may break it down. In several instances it was learned that an ideal temperature condition for a crop plant is not always the best for a disease, and vice versa.

There are certain root-rotting diseases that develop slowly at cool temperatures, and cannot cause wilt or severe effects on plants until the heat of summer. Certain fungi develop sclerotia, hard kernel-like resting bodies sometimes seen firmly adhering to plant tissues. Certain such fungus structures remain wholly dormant on contaminated seeds or in dry or cold soil. When rain and warmth arrive, the parasite grows out of the sclerotia and attacks available susceptible crop plants.

There are numerous ways in which climate affects diseases. Often powdery mildews are not seen until spring is long past and summer's rains are done. Then, with the advent of dry weather accompanied by night dews, the powdery growth comes like magic. There are regions in the tropics where the warm, heavy rains of monsoon periods are so strong and frequent that they may wash away some disease spores. On the other hand, there are diseases which are adapted to a rainy, wet environment and depend on the action of raindrops for transportation.

PROOF OF PATHOGENICITY

It is difficult to be sure that an isolated organism is a parasite, to be certain the organism causes a specific disease, and to determine whether a particular organism attacks a special species or strain of a crop plant. One needs proof; but how to obtain it? This question is critically important to plant pathologists. For a long time, lack of a recognized and dependable standard system of proof was a deterrent to the progress of the science.

In 1881, a German physician, Robert Koch, announced a series of steps used to prove that an organism is the cause of a disease. These steps in plants are as follows: *First,* the fungus or bacterium must always be found accompanying the disease. *Second,* it must be isolated from the host plant, grown by itself in pure culture, and its structure and physiology adequately described. *Third,* a representative, pure culture must be used to artificially inoculate a healthy individual and it must cause the same disease. *Finally,* the microorganism must be reisolated from the artificially infected plant and, in pure culture again, positively identified as the same organism isolated from the naturally infected plant. These clear steps can give conclusive proof that the organism causes the disease, and have been termed Koch's postulates. These postulates are used regularly in the science of plant pathology.

CROP ROTATION AND SHADE

Plant pathologists report that crop rotations may reduce disease losses at least 60 percent. This is both true and wonderful, but who first tried this method of husbandry? No one knows exactly. Judging from the testimony of successful, unschooled peasants, disease reduction by changing fields was taught to others for centuries by veteran talkative farmers. Neighbors tried it and found it a good system. Long afterwards it was tested by pathologists and put on a scientific disease-prevention basis. To be sure, pathologists, along with the agronomists and horticulturists, have worked out the scientific reasons for why the rotation of crops is desirable, and they have greatly improved crop sequences; but the idea is not a new one. It is still a valuable part of disease control now used in scientific agriculture.

A great deal of publicity has been given to the supposition that coffee is grown in the shade to produce higher quality beans. Shade actually is used only where there is sufficient rainfall; coffee grows more easily in the shade of other trees, since shade helps control disease. Under shade, dewfall is reduced, some fungus spores do not infect, plant metabolism is lessened, and although production is somewhat lowered, trees live longer and the harvest is more consistent year after year. Sun-grown coffee may produce exceptionally well at first, but the trees do this under considerable stress, and nutrients are extracted from leaf, branch, and root for the heavy load they bear. These stresses make the stems and leaves more susceptible to the *Corticium salmonicolor* pink disease, to *Cercospora* leaf spot, to *Hemileia* rust, to more branch attack by *Colletotrichum* and *Diplodia,* and to root collapse that makes them more easily infected by *Rosellinia* or *Fusarium.* Of course, coffee is not the only plantation crop grown in shade. Tea, cacao (chocolate), ginger, bananas, medicinal sources, spice trees, and Manila hemp are often healthier under shade. In the Temperate Zone, shading is restricted to special products such as wrapper tobacco, chrysanthemums, and ferns.

RESISTANCE

One of the best means of controlling plant disease has been mentioned in previous chapters—breeding crops for disease resistance. In the United States, half or more of the crops used are bred for disease resistance—in some cases, multiple resistance to several diseases in the same plant is now available. When properly developed and continually policed, this is an excellent way to fight disease, but it can run into trouble sometimes. As J. C. Walker and others have shown, in the *Fusarium* wilts of cotton, cabbage, tobacco, and, more recently, bananas, resistant varieties have been successfully developed, only to have nematode feeding injury on roots upset the whole resistance reaction. In another kind of breakdown, as in the *Puccinia graminis* rust of wheat and the two *Hemileia* rusts of coffee, in *Fusarium* wilt of tomato and in the common *Colletotrichum* anthracnose of beans, good resistance is bred into a crop. Then, as discussed in Chapter 2, a new and differently virulent race of the parasite arises by mutation. This attacks the resistant crop variety, and the whole job of getting other and better resistance has to be done over again.

CHEMICAL CONTROLS AND BORDEAUX MIXTURE

While plant pathologists were looking for ways to curb plant diseases, medical science was finding ways to use disinfectants to kill disease germs in humans. It seemed likely that the same disinfectant chemicals might work for plants, and so several were used in experiments. At first success only came in the laboratory. It was soon known that some of them, like blue vitriol (copper sulphate), corrosive sublimate (mercuric chloride), carbolic acid (phenol), sulphur, lime (sometimes called quicklime), and vinegar could be used to disinfect seeds, but were corrosive to green tissues and so of limited use.

It was the dream of the plant-disease men that someday they would have substances that killed disease germs but not green plants. This, to be ideal, would have to be applied to foliage and would stay there for reasonable lengths of time. The first piece of

luck was to find this property in one of the insecticides that was
made of a combination of lime and sulphur, which were literally
stewed together in the same pot. When used to kill insects, this
lime-sulphur mixture also had surprisingly good effects on a few
plant diseases. But the best of all the early chemicals was found
by pure accident. It is a well-known story, and a book about
plant diseases would not be worth its ink without a brief account
of the discovery of the famous Bordeaux mixture.

At the end of the nineteenth century, Europe was caught up
in a changing social order, the American and French revolutions
had come and gone, populations were increasing and on the move,
and food crops and other plant production had been neglected.
In this atmosphere, vineyard growers were having serious troubles
with their grapes. Disease was causing harvests to go down year
after year, farmers were becoming poverty stricken, and populations in Paris, Rome, Madrid, Constantinople, Lisbon, and London
faced the dismal prospect of a wine shortage. Such a shortage
naturally drew the attention of many thirsty thinkers to the problem of plant disease.

This shortage of vineyard harvest had come about from disease, but also from thievery of grapes in the French valleys of the
Dordogne and Gironde. In hopes of making their grapes less
attractive to thieves, angry vineyardists made up a poisonous-
looking concoction that stuck to leaves and that dried a vivid
light blue. Many of the growers marked the rows next to paths
as "poisonous" and spattered them with the concoction. In 1881
P. M. Alexis Millardet, a professor from the adjacent city of Bordeaux, walked along vine-lined paths, making notes of what he
observed. He saw that spattered leaves did not crumple or drop
from the chemical or from the downy mildew caused by *Plasmopara viticola*. Millardet was excited about his observation, and
he followed it up with some hard work. By 1883 he was ready to
announce that the light blue "poison" mixture could be used to
save the French vineyards. There was enthusiastic response, and
by 1885 the era of plant spraying for disease control began, using
what came to be called Bordeaux mixture.

Bordeaux mixture was, and still is, a remarkable fungicide
used all over the world on numerous of the important crops. The

agriculturists, as H. Marshall Ward predicted in the 1890s, would find that the "Bordeaux" was primarily not a cure but rather that it prevented infection. If growers sprayed their plants, the fungicide dried on foliage surfaces and stopped the fungus spores from germinating and infecting the leaves; at last there was something that killed the fungus but not the crop plant.

After about fifty years of working with Bordeaux mixture in different countries on many diseases, pathologists knew some of the things that made it a good spray. Scientists for a long time had tried without success to express in chemical formulas exactly what happened when lime and bluestone were mixed in water to make the Bordeaux mixture. Some of the chemistry is still obscure, but when sprayed onto leaves it sticks wonderfully and even kills spores at a distance from the droplets themselves on the leaves. It has many other valuable attributes, and is still a standard to which other, newer spray chemical compounds are compared.

WHAT IS A GOOD SPRAY?

What is desirable in a good spray or a good dust? It must have a differential toxicity, a kind of Jekyll-Hyde nature, by which it kills the disease organism but is relatively harmless to the crop plant. It must be a stable compound that can be shipped and stored. It must be non-poisonous to those who use it and to those who consume the sprayed product that goes to market. It must stick to plant surfaces so it will not wash off with rain, but at the same time it must be sufficiently soluble that some will be slowly released to kill infective spores. It must be a standardized material, readily obtainable and always the same. It has to be practical to apply and run through machines without excessive and recurrent difficulties. If possible, it should leave a visible residue so that the man who applies it can tell what plants have been treated. And last, it must be inexpensive enough to have an economic place in crop technology.

It is not easy for a fungicide to fulfill all these requirements. Although Bordeaux mixture is excellent, it has limitations. Some crops are injured by it, and the spray may stay on fruits or leaves as an undesirable residue. Occasionally it causes difficulty with spray equipment, and its ingredients may deteriorate under difficult storage and shipping conditions. Even using utmost care, different batches of homemade Bordeaux are not always exactly alike. The bluestone (a copper salt) is needed not only for spray but for other purposes in mountainous quantities in many parts of the world. In times of acute shortages, the price of copper is very high, and during periods of national emergency, copper is a critical necessity for wire, ammunition, and commercial machinery.

DISCOVERIES REPLACED BORDEAUX

Some time ago, therefore, agricultural scientists began serious efforts to devise spray chemicals to supplement, if not replace, Bordeaux. In 1934, a fungicide developed by the research of Wendell Tisdale and coworkers was patented. With the help of industry, these pathologists marketed the product, an organic compound and a successful spray, later called Ferbam. For some things it was as good as and for some things possibly better than Bordeaux.

This gave a tremendous boost to more scientific research on spraying and fungicides. Many new compounds were developed, and in a twenty-year period more was determined about fungicides and fungicidal action than had been learned in all previous history. The most effective fungicides are apparently best handled as proprietary materials, which means that many of these specifics for diseases are protected by copyright or patent given to concerns who formulate, manufacture, name, and guarantee the purity of composition of the compound. Because plant pathologists have more control over the fungicides' manufacture, they can prescribe them with certainty of results, having much more confidence in their effects than could be given in the Bordeaux era when homemade mixtures were common. With certain diseases, and with certain crops, certain proprietary fungicides are better able to control the disease, and they can also be used to add minor elements and aid in better finish and better color of the fruit or vegetable at harvest.

While all these innovations in spray chemicals were going on, there was equal progress in application equipment. In the old Bordeaux and lime-sulphur days, life for the spray man was hard. It required horses or tractors, barrels, mixing platforms, short-lived screens, a pond of warm water, pails or a hand pump, a spray tank on large spoked wheels, mechanical pressure pumps, rubber hoses, spray nozzles, callused hands, and a knack at directing the mist. It was not easy, a lot of water was used, and it took from three to six men—one who knew the mixing, one who handled the "rolling stock," and several to walk up and down the field putting on the spray. By the end of the day, all of them were usually well-bathed in the famous "Bordeaux blue."

Now it is different. Cab enclosures and special spray clothing protect the workers, only a fraction of the water is needed, and sometimes spray oil replaces spray water altogether. There are many other helpful innovations growing out of technical studies. Trajectories of dusts or sprays from equipment have been determined, the best droplet- or dust-particle size learned, spore flights studied, and effects of electrostatic phenomena considered. In this, statistics and theory are of important concern, based on ballistics, climatology, and aerodynamics. Working together, commercial engineers and plant pathologists are making continuous spray application advances, and manufacturers follow their work closely.

Plastics and metal alloys that are light, strong, and resistant to corrosion are now used for spraying. Engines give higher pressures than ever before, and there are spray heads available that allow a reduction of the amount of fungicide needed. Scientists are able to combine certain fungicides and insecticides with astonishingly good results. It is possible today for one man to handle the job where fields, plants, and growing practices are all adjusted to the new methods. Even the airplane is involved in spraying now, bringing with it specialized techniques, skills, split-second timing, and excitement of a far different order than anything those early users of horse- or tractor-drawn sprayers of lime-sulphur and Bordeaux might have dreamed of. Spraying has become big business.

THE MANY KINDS OF SPRAYS AND CONTROLS

The best-known kind of spraying protects leaves so they stay healthy; this is called protectant spraying. However, there are certain sprays that have the property of being absorbed by the plant and killing the disease organism growing inside foliage. The properties of these eradicant fungicides are similar to the so-called systemic insecticides that travel through a plant internally. There are also other materials called fungistats, that do not actually kill the parasite but hold it from attacking or developing.

There is not enough space to go into detail about the many measures used that control plant disease and unexpectedly early plant death. It is not all in the spraying of solutions, for dusts and gases are also used. Some discussion of certain problems will show a few types of control methods and techniques used by plant pathologists. Soil-borne nematode diseases are often controlled through volatile chemicals distributed by special methods into the soil. These chemicals also are used with other soil diseases, but it should be remembered that the disinfecting of soil is not always in itself a guarantee that there will be absolutely no disease organism in the growing field, as a great deal of infection is carried around on or in seed.

A very profitable and satisfactory method of avoiding seed-borne disease is to obtain seed from plants that are grown where the disease doesn't develop. Disease-free seed is secured where climate inhibits the development and spread of seed-carried diseases such as bean anthracnose and cabbage blackleg. Professional seed growers usually begin multiplication from a few disease-free plants in special fields, multiplying these in healthy fields, and soon produce quantities of disease-free seed for wide distribution.

Chemicals to eliminate seed contaminations are applied as solutions or dusts, and in some seed treatments disinfectants are put on as slurries, surrounding each seed with a pellet of chemical. There are volatile seed treatment materials designed to penetrate seed coats, kill or inactivate contaminating disease, and not injure the seedling. In some cases, soaking in nothing but water under special direction in employed; in others, heat is used to kill the disease-causing organisms. Although cumbersome and requiring very skillful handling, thermal treatments can be very effective, and cause no harm to the seeds or plant parts themselves. Such heat treatments can be used to eliminate virus diseases in peach trees, periwinkle, and sugar cane. A latent virus that causes no disease symptoms is sometimes present in citrus plants. If the infected trees are used for budding or grafting, the virus is carried to the new plants and breaks out with most serious consequences. The only way the latent virus problem can be solved is to eliminate the virus by heating the plant to a high temperature. After growing trees for months in heat chambers, with tops hot and roots cool, T. J. Grant and his colleagues finally obtained graft branches and budwood that were free from the virus and thereby usable for multiplication of the stock.

QUARANTINE CONTROL

Disease control is sometimes carried out by quarantine, which is the enforced isolation or exclusion of, in this case, diseased plants by nations. There are numerous examples of very bad diseases that accidentally move, often by man, from one continent to another. The grape mildew from *Plasmopara* caused little or no trouble on wild grapes in the eastern United States, but when inadvertently taken to France, it nearly ruined the wine industry until Bordeaux sprays were developed. The Dutch elm disease, caused by the fungus *Ceratostomella ulmi*, decimated the American elms in many parts of the United States, and the chestnut blight caused by *Endothia parasitica* from China was brought into the United States and has practically made the American chestnut an extinct species.

In spite of these tragedies, there are other bad diseases that have remained within their regions of origin and luckily have not spread anywhere else. The *Hemileia vastatrix* rust of coffee in Africa and the Orient had not been established on coffee in the American tropics until the last few years. The South American *Dothidella* rubber leaf disease is still only in the American tropics and has not reached the Orient or Africa. It is obviously worth a great deal to keep such plant diseases from being moved around for as long as possible by employing strict quarantine.

The word quarantine is commonplace in plant pathology. In the old Latin and French it refers to the forty days a possibly infected ship was forced to wait at anchor before it could touch port to insure that no foreign diseases were brought ashore. There are two notable features in plant quarantine: First, the isolation of suspicious plants under careful surveillance so that if disease is present, other plants do not catch the disease. Second, the introduced plants are kept isolated, waiting a sufficiently long time for an incubation period to allow disease to appear. If it does develop it can be eliminated before it spreads. Quarantine operated in this manner can, in some cases, be a practical means of disease control. Knowing this, states, provinces, nations, and international communities of nations have enforcement officers who legally enforce plant quarantines.

By quarantines against special diseases, vast field enterprises are preserved. There was the long-time successful quarantine by Western Hemisphere coffee growers against rust, which once destroyed the immensely profitable Oriental and African coffee production. An adequate quarantine, based on knowledge not available in the first part of the last century, might have saved millions of lives and prevented the mass migrations that resulted from the potato blight that devastated Ireland and England. The United States has especially strict quarantines against a number of dreaded foreign plant disease nematodes. Quarantine regulations are designed to halt the spread of such disease organisms. In all likelihood, despite great care, virtually any plant disease will in the long run find its way through the strictest quarantines. But the quarantines are still worthwhile, since to keep a disease away for a number of years, decades, or a century gives those responsible for the health of crops a breathing spell. It gives pathologists the time they need to study the troubles and to develop control measures in regions where the disease is endemic. These treatments can then be used when the disease eventually spreads.

RELATIVE QUARANTINE EFFECTIVENESS

The effectiveness of a quarantine depends on the kind of disease it is supposed to control. A quarantine will have the most success with a disease normally spread by human activity. The Dutch elm disease is an example. It was unwittingly taken to the United States from Europe in elm logs shipped for veneer. The highly destructive golden nematode, *Heterodera rostochiensis,* is carried to new areas in contaminated soil, wrappings, and infected plants. There is also the banana wilt disease from the fungus *Fusarium oxysporum cubense* that is readily transferred from place to place in live planting materials. All of these diseases can be stopped by preventing people from transporting the host plants or soil.

Much more difficult to control are those diseases that occur widely, do not need to be spread, and are thus already on hand. In such as these, quarantines may have minor local value at best. The soil-inhabiting damping-off fungus, *Rhizoctonia solani,* is so wide in occurrence that quarantines against it have little practical effect. The bacterial slimy soft-rot organism, *Erwinia carotovora,* is well-nigh ubiquitous. The same is generally true about *Glomerella cingulata.* The gray mold rots and stem rots of various hosts caused by *Botrytis* occur in very different parts of the world, live on dead plants, and are forever causing disease in living crops.

Quarantines are also of little effect in diseases carried around by winds which no possible deflective or holding measure can stop. Wheat rust is one of these whose spores are taken everywhere on earth. Powdery mildews such as *Erysiphe cichoracearum* attack a wide range of plant species and cannot be limited because their lightweight spores are so readily picked up by the breezes. Seed spots and death from the yeast, *Nematospora,* are widely spread via contaminated bills of sucking bugs that travel about without any chance of international control.

While Nature thus frustrates some of man's attempts at quarantine, she has some quarantine devices of her own. There are geographical and climatological features of the earth that act as exclusion corridors between regions and so limit disease spread between cultivated lands, such as the Pacific and the Atlantic oceans. Turbulent airs over mountain ridges hinder some long-distance spore travel. In the United States the north and south stretch of the Rocky Mountains effectively separates diseases on the West Coast from the central plains. The multiple parallel ridges of the Appalachians cut off the eastern seaboard diseases from the Midwest. Deserts act as exclusion corridors, as do vast seas of green rain forest in the tropics. Disease spores, picked up and started across all such corridors, may fall into areas where they cannot live and in this way disappear.

QUARANTINE OF ASTRONAUTS AGAINST BRINGING BACK CONTAMINATION

Just as distances do on Earth, distances between planets remain effective barriers of plant disease interchange. With the coming of the Space Age, however, the prospect of the accidental introduction onto Earth of possible plant diseases from other planets is frightening. Astronauts returning to Earth from the Moon, Mars, or other planets could be agents bringing back contamination to Earth. Any organisms outside the influence of Earth may depend on principles of growth not now conceivable by Earth's inhabitants. Such a contamination might not be necessarily a virus, bacterium, or fungus, but some entity or organism with possibilities far different from anything humanity has ever encountered. Such a thing from another planet could soon result in complete destruction of all plant life—and, therefore, of all human and animal life.

In recent Moon exploration, astronauts and their gear were subjected to strictest decontamination and quarantine procedures when they returned to Earth. Although there are rare possibilities that living entities occur on the Moon's apparently sterile surface and in its forbidding environment, scientists here on Earth had to eliminate any chance that the explorers might have brought back with them some kind of disease. Under strictest protection to keep possible contamination from being spread outside, plants were grown in Moon soil in enclosed cabinets. Samples of the soil were used to inoculate plant leaves, stems, and roots to determine if diseases might develop. Moon walkers, before they returned to Earth, changed clothes and left on the lunar surface any extra-terrestrial-tainted boots, gloves, suits, tools, or life-sustaining apparatus. When the men returned to Earth, even with new shoes known to be moon-dirt-free, their footprints leading to the quarantine chamber were immediately washed down and sprayed with decontaminating solutions. It was only after weeks under most careful quarantine and daily health examinations that the isolation was broken and the explorers were finally allowed to walk free among other human beings, and to come into contact with plants on Earth.

SUGGESTED SOURCES

FOR FURTHER READING

Gordon A. Brandes et al. *Compendium of Plant Diseases*. Philadelphia: Rohm & Haas, 1959. 264 pages.

Edwin J. Butler and S. G. Jones. *Plant Pathology*. London: Macmillan, 1949. 979 pages.

Charles Chupp and Arden F. Sherf. *Vegetable Diseases and Their Control*. New York: Ronald Press, 1960. 693 pages.

J. George Harrar. *Strategy for the Conquest of Hunger*. New York: The Rockefeller Foundation, 1963. 117 pages.

E. C. Large. *The Advance of the Fungi*. New York: Dover Publications, Inc., 1962. 488 pages.

Pascal P. Pirone, Bernard O. Dodge, and Harold W. Rickett. *Diseases and Pests of Ornamental Plants* (Third Edition). New York: Ronald Press, 1960. 776 pages.

Malcom C. Shurtleff. *How to Control Plant Diseases in Home and Garden*. Ames, Iowa: Iowa State University Press, 1962. 520 pages.

Elvin C. Stakman and J. George Harrar. *Principles of Plant Pathology*. New York: Ronald Press, 1957. 581 pages.

U. S. Department of Agriculture. *Plant Diseases*. U. S. Department of Agriculture Yearbook, 1953.

U. S. Department of Agriculture, Crops Research Division. *Index of Plant Diseases in the United States.* Agricultural Handbook No. 165, 1960. 531 pages.

J. E. VanDer Plank, *Plant Diseases: Epidemics and Control.* New York: Academic Press, 1963. 349 pages.

John Charles Walker. *Plant Pathology* (Third Edition). New York: McGraw-Hill, 1969. 819 pages.

George S. Wells. *Garden in the West: A Dramatic Account of Science in Agriculture.* New York: Dodd, Mead & Co., 1969. 270 pages.

Cecil Woodham-Smith. *The Great Hunger, Ireland 1845–1849.* New York and Evanston: Harper & Row Publishers, 1962. 510 pages.

There are numerous other books on plant diseases in several languages, dating from about the beginning third of the nineteenth century, at first, of course, from Europe. There are several scientific magazines that are continuously publishing articles about plant diseases; probably the best known is "Phytopathology" the international journal of the American Phytopathological Society. Thousands of special bulletins and scientific papers about problems on plant diseases have been, and are being, published in many parts of the world, coming from national, state, and private institutions.

ADDITIONAL READING

Chapter 1

Clyde M. Christensen. *The Molds and Man.* Minneapolis: University of Minnesota Press, 1966. 284 pages.

N. R. Danielian. "To Win the Fight Against World Starvation." *Reader's Digest,* August 1966. Pp. 70–74.

William D. Gray. *The Relation of Fungi to Human Affairs.* New York: Henry Holt & Co., 1959. 510 pages.

Lucy Kavaler. *Mushrooms, Molds, and Miracles; The Strange Realm of Fungi.* New York: John Day Company, 1965. 318 pages.

Harold H. McKinney. *Foot-rot Diseases of Wheat in America.* U. S. Department of Agriculture, Bulletin 1347, 1925. 40 pages.

George L. McNew. "Pathology." *Encyclopedia Americana,* Vol. 22, 1964. Pp. 198–202.

William and Paul Paddock. "They Can't Eat Our Know-How." (Condensed from the book *Hungry Nations*) *Reader's Digest,* June 1965. Pp. 83–86.

A. J. Riker. "Plant Pathology and Human Welfare." *Science,* Vol. 152. Pp. 1027–32.

Nevin S. Scrimshaw. "Food." *Scientific American,* Vol. 209. Pp. 72–80.

E. C. Stakman and Donald G. Fletcher. *The Common Barberry and Black Stem Rust.* U. S. Department of Agriculture, Bulletin 1544, 1930. 28 pages.

John Strohm. "Mexico Closes the Food Gap." *Reader's Digest,* June 1966. Pp. 165–72.

Jessie I. Wood. "Three Billion Dollars a Year," *Plant Diseases,* U. S. Department of Agriculture Yearbook, 1953. P. 109.

CHAPTER 2

James G. Dickson. *Diseases of Field Crops* (Second Edition). New York: McGraw-Hill, 1956. 517 pages.

R. W. Leukel and V. F. Tapke. *Barley Diseases and Their Control.* U. S. Department of Agriculture, Farmer's Bulletin 2089, 1955. 28 pages.

John H. Martin and S. C. Salmon. "The Rusts of Wheat, Oats, Barley, and Rye." *Plant Diseases,* U. S. Department of Agriculture Yearbook, 1953. Pp. 329–43.

Frederick L. Wellman. "Some Important Diseases of Coffee." *Plant Diseases,* U. S. Department of Agriculture Yearbook, 1953. Pp. 891–96.

S. A. Wingard. "The Nature of Resistance to Disease." *Plant Diseases,* U. S. Department of Agriculture Yearbook, 1953. Pp. 165–73.

CHAPTER 3

Robert A. Conover. "Antibiotic Spray Halts Bacterial Disease." *Florists' Review,* Vol. 114, August 12, 1954. Pp. 53–54.

A. W. Dimock and L. A. McFadden. "Bacterial Mum Disease." *Florists' Review,* Vol. 114, April 29, 1954. Pp. 17–18.

Stewart A. Koser. "Bacteriology." *Encyclopaedia Britannica,* Vol. 2, 1963. Pp. 1009–20.

Perry W. Wilson and Joe B. Wilson. "Bacteria and Bacteriology." *Encyclopedia Americana,* Vol. 3, 1964. Pp. 27–35a.

Elie L. Wollman and François Jacob. "Sexuality in Bacteria." *Scientific American,* Vol. 195, July 1956. Pp. 109–18.

CHAPTER 4

F. C. Bawden. *Plant Viruses and Virus Diseases.* New York: Ronald Press, 1964. 361 pages.

C. W. Bennett. "Viruses, a Scourge of Mankind." *Plant Diseases,* U. S. Department of Agriculture Yearbook, 1953. Pp. 15–22.

Philip Brierley and Paul Lorentz. "Hydrangea Ringspot." *Florists' Review,* Vol. 119, May 14, 1957. Pp. 113–15.

Heinz Frankel-Conrat. "The Genetic Code of a Virus." *Scientific American,* Vol. 211, October 1964. Pp. 47–55.

R. W. Horne, "The Structure of Viruses." *Scientific American,* Vol. 208, January 1963. Pp. 48–66.

Isabel M. Mountain. "Virus." *Encyclopedia Americana,* Vol. 28, 1964. Pp. 169–71.

CHAPTER 5

John Tyler Bonner. "The Growth of Mushrooms." *Scientific American,* Vol. 194, May 1956. Pp. 97–106.

Victor R. Boswell, S. P. Doolittle, and L. M. Pultz. *Pepper Production, Disease and Insect Control.* U. S. Department of Agriculture, Farmer's Bulletin 2051, 1952. 30 pages.

E. E. Clayton and J. E. McMurtrey, Jr. *Tobacco Diseases and Their Control.* U. S. Department of Agriculture, Farmer's Bulletin 2023, 1950. 69 pages.

Richard H. Converse. *Diseases of Raspberries and Erect and Trailing Blackberries.* U. S. Department of Agriculture, Handbook No. 310, 1966. 111 pages.

Ralph Emerson. "Molds and Men." *Scientific American,* Vol. 186, January 1952. Pp. 28–32.

K. W. Kreitlow and F. V. Juska. *Lawn Diseases: How to Control Them.* U. S. Department of Agriculture, Home and Garden Bulletin 61, 1963. 16 pages.

George K. K. Link and Glen B. Ramsey. *Market Diseases of Fruit and Vegetables; Potatoes.* U. S. Department of Agriculture, Miscellaneous Publication 98, 1932. 62 pages.

John S. Niederhauser and William C. Cobb. "The Late Blight." *Scientific American,* Vol. 200, May 1959. Pp. 100–12.

Lindsay S. Olive. "Fungi." *Encyclopedia Americana,* Vol. 12, 1964. Pp. 164–72.

Willis Peterson. "Fungi, Friend or Foe?" *Arizona Highways,* Vol. 36, October 1960. Pp. 30–39.

Glen B. Ramsey et al. *Market Diseases of Fruits and Vegetables.* U. S. Department of Agriculture, Miscellaneous Publication 292, 1938; and Miscellaneous Publication 541, 1944.

Glen B. Ramsey, James S. Wiant, and Lacy P. McCulloch. *Market Diseases of Tomatoes, Peppers, and Eggplants.* U. S. Department of Agriculture, Handbook No. 28, 1952. 54 pages.

Glen B. Ramsey and M. A. Smith. "Market Diseases Caused by Fungi." *Plant Diseases,* U. S. Department of Agriculture Yearbook, 1953. Pp. 809–16.

R. P. Scheffer and W. J. Haney. "Root Rot." *Florists' Review,* Vol. 119, November 22, 1958. Pp. 98–100.

Russell B. Stevens. "Fungi are Living Organisms." *Plant Diseases,* U. S. Department of Agriculture Yearbook, 1953. Pp. 27–31.

Richard J. Tabor et al. "Fungi." *Encyclopaedia Britannica,* Vol. 9, 1963. Pp. 922–34.

U. S. Agricultural Research Service. *Chestnut Blight and Resistant Chestnuts.* U. S. Department of Agriculture, Farmer's Bulletin 2068, 1954. 21 pages.

Charles Morrow Wilson. "The Case of the Bad Nematode." *Reader's Digest,* January 1961. Pp. 189–92.

Chapter 6

Anonymous. "Mistletoe." *Encyclopaedia Britannica,* Vol. 15, 1963. Pp. 616–17.

J. H. Dawson, W. O. Lee, and F. L. Timmons. *Controlling Dodder in Alfalfa.* U. S. Department of Agriculture, Farmer's Bulletin 2211, 1965. 16 pages.

R. F. Scharpf and J. R. Parmeter, Jr. *The Biology and Pathology of Dwarfmistletoe Arceuthobium campylopodium f. abietinum Parasitizing True Firs (Abies spp.) in California.* U. S. Department of Agriculture, Technical Bulletin 1362, 1967. 42 pages.

Norman Taylor. "Dodder." *Encyclopaedia Britannica,* Vol. 7, 1963. P. 538.

Willis W. Wagener. "Parasitic Plants." *Encyclopaedia Britannica,* Vol. 17, 1963. Pp. 279–80.

CHAPTER 7

Grace Griggs Cottrell. "Flower Producers Lose Millions of Dollars from Polluted Air." *Florist and Nursery Exchange,* January 16, 1968. Pp. 5–8.

R. D. Dickey. "Freezing Injury to Foliage Plants." *Florists' Review,* Vol. 115, November 11, 1954. P. 38.

J. E. McMurtrey, Jr. "Environmental, Nonparasitic Injuries." *Plant Diseases,* U. S. Department of Agriculture Yearbook, 1953. Pp. 101–14.

George L. McNew. "The Effects of Soil Fertility." *Plant Diseases,* U. S. Department of Agriculture Yearbook, 1953. Pp. 101–14.

J. J. Oertli. "Azalea Nutrition Disorders." *Florists' Review,* Vol. 125, August 20, 1964. Pp. 20–26; August 27, 1964. Pp. 21, 62–63; September 3, 1964. Pp. 31 and 80.

Freeman A. Weiss. "Ailments of House Plants." *Plant Diseases,* U. S. Department of Agriculture Yearbook, 1953. Pp. 858–61.

T. R. Wright. "Physiological Disorders." *Plant Diseases,* U. S. Department of Agriculture Yearbook, 1953. Pp. 830–34.

CHAPTER 8

John G. Atkins. *Rice Diseases.* U. S. Department of Agriculture, Farmer's Bulletin 2120, 1958. 14 pages.

J. M. Dunleavy, D. W. Chamberlain, and J. P. Ross. *Soybean Diseases.* U. S. Department of Agriculture, Handbook No. 302, 1966. 38 pages.

William Hovanitz. "Insects and Plant Galls." *Scientific American,* Vol. 201, November 1959. Pp. 151–62.

K. W. Kreitlow and F. V. Tapke. *Lawn Diseases, How to Control Them.* U. S. Department of Agriculture, Home and Garden Bulletin 61, 1960. 16 pages.

John R. McGrew. *Strawberry Diseases.* U. S. Department of Agriculture, Farmer's Bulletin 2140, 1959. 24 pages.

L. M. Massey. "Four Diseases of Garden Roses." *Plant Diseases,* U. S. Department of Agriculture Yearbook, 1953. Pp. 625–36.

L. B. Reed and S. P. Doolittle. *Insects and Diseases of Vegetables in the Home Garden.* U. S. Department of Agriculture, Home and Garden Bulletin 46, 1958. 48 pages.

Marion A. Smith, Lacy P. McCulloch, and Bernard A. Friedman. *Market Diseases of Asparagus, Onions, Beans, Peas, Carrots, Celery, and Related Vegetables.* U. S. Department of Agriculture, Handbook No. 303, 1966. 65 pages.

Lee Templeton. "Can Our Oaks Survive?" *Reader's Digest.* January 1953. Pp. 63–64. (Condensed from *Harper's* magazine, November 1952.)

H. Rex Thomas and W. J. Zaumeyer. "Developing Healthier Vegetables." *Plant Diseases,* U. S. Department of Agriculture Yearbook, 1953. Pp. 493–508.

Eugene H. Varney. "Strawberry Killer." *American Fruit Grower,* Vol. 83, June 1960. Pp. 24–25.

W. J. Zaumeyer and H. Rex Thomas. "Field Diseases of Beans and Lima Beans." *Plant Diseases,* U. S. Department of Agriculture Yearbook, 1953. Pp. 393–400.

CHAPTER 9

Joseph C. Chamberlain et al. *Studies of Airplane Spray-Deposit Patterns at Low Flight Levels.* U. S. Department of Agriculture, Technical Bulletin 1110, 1955. 45 pages.

Crops Research Division. *Controlling Diseases of Raspberries and Blackberries.* U. S. Department of Agriculture, Farmer's Bulletin 2208, 1965. 16 pages.

Crops Research Division. *Controlling Tomato Diseases.* U. S. Department of Agriculture, Farmer's Bulletin 2200, 1966. 12 pages.

J. C. Fevmas. "They are Bringing Back the Chestnut Tree." *Reader's Digest.* April 1963. Pp. 129–32.

Charles J. Gould. "Control of Blue Mold on Iris." *Florists' Review,* Vol. 115, March 10, 1955. Pp. 114–15.

Harold J. Jensen. "Control of Nematodes Through Fumigation." *Florists' Review,* Vol. 114, June 3, 1954. Pp. 108–10.

R. W. Leukel. "Treating Seeds to Prevent Diseases." *Plant Diseases,* U. S. Department of Agriculture Yearbook, 1953. Pp. 134–45.

J. R. McGrew, G. W. Still, and Howard Baker. *Control of Grape Diseases and Insects in the Eastern United States.* U. S. Department of Agriculture, Farmer's Bulletin 1893, 1961. 31 pages.

W. F. Mai and K. G. Parker. "Nematodes, How They Affect Tree Growth." *American Fruit Grower,* Vol. 82, February 1962. Pp. 46–48.

Charles R. Phillips and Robert K. Hoffman. "Sterilization of Interplanetary Vehicles." *Science,* Vol. 132, October 14, 1960. Pp. 991–95.

Dwight Powell. "New Varieties Create New Disease Problems." *American Fruit Grower,* Vol. 81, February 12, 1961. Pp. 54–55.

Saul Rich. "Botrytis Control on Roses in Storage." *Florists' Review,* Vol. 115, September 23, 1954. P. 61.

Eric G. Sharvelle. "What's New in Fungicides?" *American Fruit Grower,* Vol. 82, February 1962. Pp. 30, 71–72.

INDEX